Build Your Own

Grandfather
Clock

and Save

Build Your Own

Grandfather Clock

and Save

John A. Nelson

TAB BOOKS Inc.
Blue Ridge Summit, PA

FIRST EDITION
FIRST PRINTING

Library of Congress Cataloging in Publication Data

Nelson, John A., 1935-
Build your own grandfather clock and save /by John A. Nelson.
        p.   cm.
     ISBN 0-8306-9053-0   ISBN 0-8306-9353-X (pbk.)
    1. Clock and watch making. 2. Longcase clocks. I. Title.
             TS545.N44 1988
     681.1′13—dc19   88-20151
                                                          CIP

TAB BOOKS Inc. offers software for sale. For information and a catalog, please
contact TAB Software Department, Blue Ridge Summit, PA 17294-0850.

Questions regarding the content of this book
should be addressed to:

Reader Inquiry Branch
TAB BOOKS Inc.
Blue Ridge Summit, PA 17294-0214

Contents

Introduction

Building a grandfather clock has always been an extremely complicated project and, up to this time, beyond the ability of the average woodworker. With all the many interlocking pieces, special moldings, and complicated jointery, it is difficult to understand just how a grandfather clock is assembled.

This book has been written and illustrated to change all that. It reduces a grandfather clock to its individual components so that even the novice woodworker can build this grandfather clock. Thumb through this book and you will find each and every part has been fully illustrated and dimensioned. Every potential problem has been anticipated. Photographs have been added to further help you visualize what is to be done and how to do it. To date, at least eight clocks have been built with these plans—including one built from scratch by three high school sophomores in their Woodworking II shop class. The students had only 1 year of woodworking experience; however, by using these drawings of individual parts, they had very few problems constructing this clock. In fact, if you take care in making and sanding each part according to the plans, the clock should go together as easily as a clock kit.

Also, by making and assembling this grandfather clock, you will have gained the knowledge of how most other grandfather clocks are made. You should be able to understand the plans for any clock you wish to build in the future. Building this clock is not really difficult, and your finished clock will be well worth your time and effort. More importantly, you will have the satisfaction of knowing you have built, from scratch, one of the most challenging woodworking projects there is to build. This is a special woodworking project that will probably last much longer than you will. It will gain in value through the years and can be passed on to your children and to their children—a truly prized possession.

In addition, there are economic advantages in building your own clock. The price of an antique grandfather clock is extremely prohibitive. The original of this particular model would probably cost over $10,000—if it could be purchased at all. Today, good reproductions cost over $1,800 and probably have plywood or pressboard backs. There are some very nice grandfather clock kits available that are reasonably priced—but with a clock kit, you can never really say, "I made this clock myself."

The case of this clock will cost from $65 to $160, depending on what kind of wood is used. If you choose maple, the wood used for the original, the case will cost around $98 to make. Hinges, glass, door locks, and miscellaneous brass material will bring the cost up another $20 to $35. A good quality, bell-strike, grandfather-clock movement will cost from $175 to $425, depending upon your choice. The total estimated cost for this clock, with the $425 movement, is $600—much less if you choose the $175 movement. Add to this the pride of building a grandfather clock like this one and the cost is very low indeed.

The overall case design of this very old grandfather clock was taken from two or three clocks originally built around 1745 by Nathaniel Mulliken of Lexington, Massachusetts. It was chosen because of its flat-top hood. Nathaniel's clocks tended to be a little shorter than most tall case clocks of that day, so I added 8 inches to his original design. The original was 80 inches tall and this copy has been extended to 88 inches tall. Those wishing to be 100 percent authentic (or who have low ceilings in their homes) should shorten their clocks by 8 inches at the waist.

Nathaniel Mulliken was born August 8, 1722, in Bradford, Massachusetts. In 1750, Mulliken moved to Lexington, Massachusetts, where he set up a clock-making shop. It is said that Mulliken worked with Benjamin Willard, a very famous clockmaker of that time, in Lexington. Mulliken died in November of 1767 at the age of 45. His clock-making business was passed down to his son, Nathaniel II. On April 19, 1775, the Mulliken clock shop was burned down by the British troops during their retreat to Boston. After losing his home and shop, Nathaniel II moved to Concord, Massachusetts.

I have written this book with great respect and admiration for Nathaniel Mulliken and the craftsmen of his day. I hope today's woodworker will get to know and understand their genius.

Dedication

To Edward ''Pete'' Racine of St. Johnsbury, Vermont—
a life-long friend and horologist.

Acknowledgments

Special appreciation and thanks go to William Bigelow and
his students at Conval Regional High School, Peterborough, N.H.
for their help and input in writing this book.

Section I

HISTORICAL BACKGROUND

Historical
Background

IN 1580 OR SO THE ASTRONOMER GALILEO OBSERVED A SWINGING LAMP SUS-
pended by a long chain from a cathedral ceiling. He studied its swing
and discovered that each swing was equal and had a natural rate of
motion. He later found this rate of motion depended upon the length
of the chain or pendulum. Many years later, in 1640, he designed a clock
mechanism incorporating the swing of a pendulum but died before
building his clock design. Later, in 1656, Christian Huygens added a
pendulum to a clock mechanism of his own design and found it kept
excellent time. Regulating the speed of the movement was done, as it
is today, by simply raising or lowering the pendulum bob—*up* to speed
up the clock, *down* to slow down the clock—thus the terms ''speed up''
and ''slow down.''
Note: the *length* of a pendulum is usually considered to be the length from
the center of the shaft that holds the hands to the center of the pendulum
bob. Sometimes it is measured from the center of the shaft that holds
the hands to the bottom tip of the pendulum bob.

Early Mechanical Clocks

The very first early mechanical clocks, less pendulums, were developed
in the last half of the thirteenth century, probably by monks from central

Europe, and were placed within the church. They did not have dials or hands and only struck bells on the hour. These mechanical devices were most likely placed in the church belfry in order to make use of the existing church bell. It was over 100 years before visible dials and hands were added. These early clocks were very large and were made of heavy iron frames and gears forged by local blacksmiths.

By the first part of the fifteenth century, small domestic clocks started to appear. They were probably made by the local gunsmiths or locksmiths. After 1630, a weight-driven lantern clock became popular for the home use of the very wealthy. When the swinging pendulum was added in 1656, the clocks became more accurate. Very early clock movements were mounted high above the floor because they required long pendulums and large cast-iron descending weights. In reality, they were nothing more than simple mechanical works with a face and hands hung on the wall. They were referred to as "wags-on-the-wall." The long-case, or grand-father, clock actually evolved from these early wag-on-the wall prototypes. Wooden cases were used only to hide the unsightly weights and cast-iron pendulums.

Clocks in the Colonies

Clocks were first brought to the American Colonies in the early 1600s by wealthy colonists. To the early colonist, owning a clock was more a mark of success than a commitment to punctuality. A clock was found in the finest homes and always displayed in a prominent place. Most people of that time could not afford a clock of their own and had to rely on the church clock on the common for the time of day.

Most early clockmakers were not skilled in wood techniques and, therefore, turned to jointers for their woodworking abilities. These early jointers used the exact same jointing techniques and styles that they used on furniture. It was not until 1683 that the first immigrant, William Davis, claimed to be a clockmaker. By 1799, the number of clocks attracted horological artisans to the New World. Most of these early artisans settled in populous centers such as Boston and Philadelphia. Later, others came to New York, Charlestown, Baltimore, and New Haven.

The handcrafting of clocks grew in all areas of the eastern part of the colonies. At the beginning of the eighteenth century, there were many makes of long-case clocks in the Quaker colony of Pennsylvania. The earliest clockmakers from Philadelphia were Samuel Bispham, Alel Cottey, and Peter Stretch. The most famous clockmaker of Philadelphia was David Rittenhouse. Rittenhouse succeeded Benjamin Franklin as president of the American Philosophical Society and later became director of the United States Mint.

Nineteenth-Century Grandfather Clocks

After 1800, inexpensive tall-case clocks were made in quantity and were affordable to more and more people. The clock-making industry spread to Massachusetts, Connecticut, New Hampshire, Rhode Island, and Vermont. In Massachusetts, Benjamin and Ephrim Willard became very famous for their exceptionally beautiful long-case clocks. In Connecticut, the first successful, domestic, mass-produced long-case clocks were developed by Eli Terry. In those days, most clock cases were made by local cabinet makers. The works, either brass or wood, were made by the firm that specialized in clockworks. The cabinet maker engraved or painted *his* name on the dial, thereby taking the claim for the completed clock.

When the industrial revolution came about, along with regular factory working hours and the introduction of train schedules, the necessity for standardized timekeeping really brought clock making to the fore. The term, "grandfather clock," now in general use, replaced the old terms, "tall-case," "hall," "floor," and "long-case" clock.

Movements Used In Early Clocks

Early American grandfather clocks contained one of the following types of brass or wooden movements:

Brass Movements

- ☐ One-day (30-hour), one weight, key wind
- ☐ Eight-day, two weights, key wind (movement required for the clock in this book)
- ☐ Eight-day, spring powered, key wind (very rare in later years—most were weight driven)

Wooden Movements

- ☐ One-day (30-hour), one weight, pull wind
- ☐ One-day (30-hour), two weights, key wind or pull wind
- ☐ Eight-day, two weights, key wind or pull wind (very rare)

Assembled clock has an 8-day, weight-driven movement with a rack and snail bell strike.

Note: Most early American grandfather clocks did not have chimes. Also, some pull wind clocks had false key wind holes painted on the face to give the illusion it was a key wind clock.

Traits and Assembly of Early Clocks

Most early grandfather clocks had a time and strike movement, generally striking only on the hour on a large 4-inch or 5-inch cast-iron bell. Pendulums and weights were very coarse, unfinished, and made of cast iron. Pendulum length was usually 42 inches long. Because glass was very expensive and the pendulums and weights were not very nice to look at, all early clocks were made with a solid front door.

Nails were used to hold early clocks together. Glue probably would not have been used, as it was hard to obtain. When the original of this clock was made, nails were hand-forged from pure iron. This made them rust-resistant and relatively pliable; they bent easily but seldom broke. These nails were probably either the rose-head type or completely headless. Because these early nails were hand-forged, no two nails were exactly the same.

The front of the case of this original clock was nailed together. Therefore, as much as I hated to, I nailed my case together in the same locations as Nathaniel did, using square-cut nails. Today this looks crude—but, it *is* authentic.

Screws were used as early as 1700 and, although I could not find them, there probably would have been some screws used in the original of this clock. The first screws were made by hand and were much more expensive to make than nails; therefore, they were used less frequently. Most early screws were only ½ inch in length or shorter. Their threads were made by hand and were very uneven and wide with rounded edges. The tips of these early screws were always blunt and usually off center.

Section II

BEFORE YOU BEGIN

Before You Begin

BEFORE YOU BEGIN YOUR CLOCK, YOU SHOULD BE FAMILIAR WITH CERTAIN basics of clock construction. This section includes fundamental information beginning with the components of the long-case clock. (The glossary at the end of the book will help you to recognize some of the terms used.) In addition, this chapter contains lists of tools and materials needed to build this replica, as well as instructions on interpreting the illustrations in this book.

Long-Case Clock Components

The long-case clock consists of the case, the movement, and accessories such as a winding key (for key wind clocks) and a case door key. Each will be discussed below.

The Case

The *case* consists of the base, waist, and hood. Some early makers of grandfather clock cases also added feet, waist and door columns, and hood fret work with finials (Illus. A). Cases were made of many kinds of wood, although hardwoods such as maple, cherry, walnut, and mahogany were usually used. Mahogany was considered the most elegant

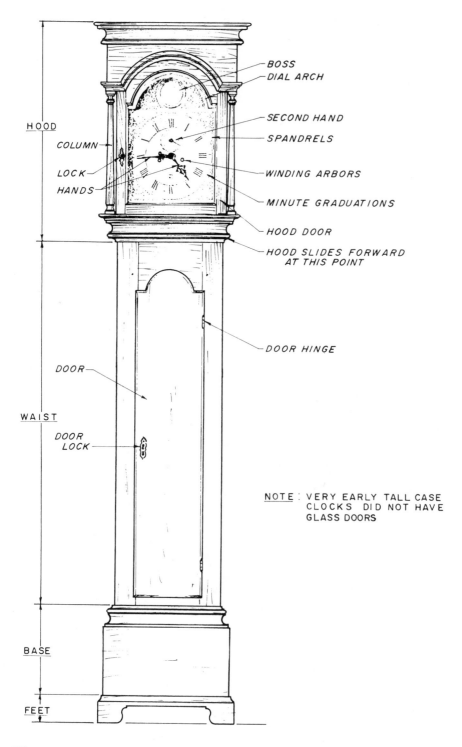

BOSS
DIAL ARCH

SECOND HAND

SPANDRELS

WINDING ARBORS

MINUTE GRADUATIONS

HOOD DOOR

HOOD SLIDES FORWARD
AT THIS POINT

DOOR HINGE

HOOD

COLUMN

LOCK

HANDS

WAIST

DOOR

DOOR
LOCK

BASE

FEET

NOTE : VERY EARLY TALL CASE
CLOCKS DID NOT HAVE
GLASS DOORS

Illus. A. Components of the long-case clock.

wood. To lower the cost, some clockmakers used pine and added a painted grain to simulate the more desired and expensive hardwoods.

Many grandfather clock cases were very elegant and beautiful while others were extremely crude. Around the turn of the century, in their heyday, many grandfather clocks were built 9 feet or more in height. Most grandfather clocks today range from 6 feet to 7 feet, 6 inches with some as tall as 8 feet. To be considered a grandfather clock, a clock must be at least 6 feet in height. Tall-case clocks below this height are considered grandmother clocks. Cases often reflected the styles of the period, including Chippendale, Sheraton, and Hepplewhite.

The Movement

The brass movement of most original grandfather clocks consists of two brass plates approximately ⅛-inch thick and 5 × 7 inches in size. The plates are spaced about 2 inches apart. There are usually nine shafts, or *arbors*, that contain seven large gears, or *wheels*, and six smaller pinion gears. Mounted on the front plate are two pinion gears that regulate the movement of the two hands. Located outside the plates, just behind the two front gears, is a mechanism to index the correct number of striking blows to the bell on the hour only. Two mechanisms frequently used to control the strike are the *count-wheel system* and the more elaborate, self-correcting system known as the *rack and snail* (Illus. B). Early original movements usually had a cast-iron bell mounted on top and most did *not* have a chiming movement.

Because most early grandfather clocks were weight-driven, springs were not usually used. Most have two weights, one weight to run the clock and the other to run the strike mechanism. A different number of teeth must be used on each gear (wheel) in order to produce a gear reduction so the weight cannot fall too fast. The final escapement wheel of a typical clock movement rotates over 10,000 times a week, while the winding gear that the weight is attached to rotates only about 15 times a week. Speed is actually controlled by the escapement gear and verge which allows the escapement gear to advance only *one* tooth per swing of the pendulum (Illus. C). It is the crutch that provides the "kick" to keep the pendulum in motion. Grandfather clocks usually use a 42-inch pendulum length with a simple wooden pendulum rod and rough cast-iron pendulum bob.

Wooden works are very similar to the brass works in design and function just as well. Most use the count-wheel system to regulate the strike mechanism but are only 30-hour clocks and, therefore, need winding every day. Some parts related to the movement were not made by the early clockmakers. Items such as hands, weights, pendulum bobs, and finials were purchased from England.

STRIKING CONTROLS

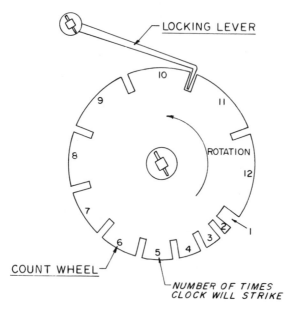

COUNT WHEEL

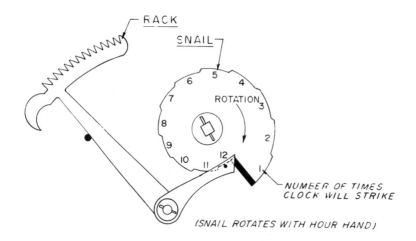

RACK AND SNAIL

Illus. B. Strike control mechanisms.

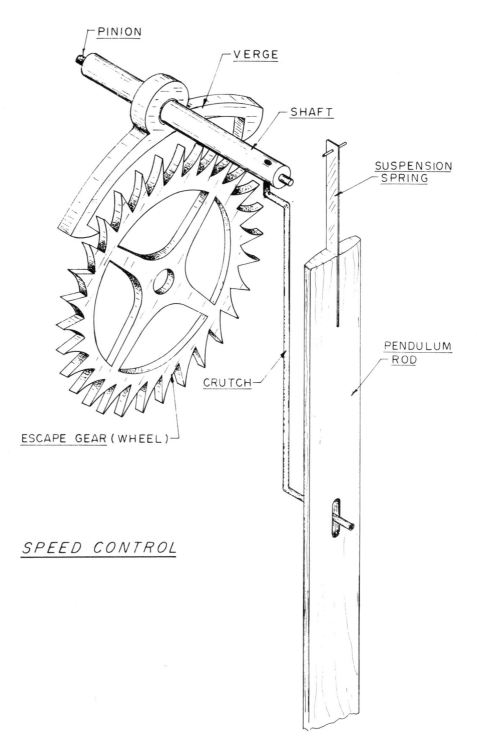

PINION

VERGE

SHAFT

SUSPENSION
SPRING

CRUTCH

PENDULUM
ROD

ESCAPE GEAR (WHEEL)

SPEED CONTROL

Illus. C. Speed control mechanisms.

Dials and Clock Accessories

Dials and accessories such as winding keys and case and door locks with keys were also purchased in England during the 1700s. Dials are divided into two basic kinds—brass and painted dials. Elaborately engraved brass dials with raised numbers were used exclusively in America until 1775. White-painted dials with painted decorations were imported from England and by 1800 had just about replaced the brass dial. These painted dials were much cheaper to produce and, therefore, more popular with clockmakers. As time went by, America produced painted dials of their own.

Roman numerals were used on most dials of the early period; Arabic numerals were very seldom used. The use of Roman numerals is probably attributable to the fact that all documents used Roman numerals up to 1700. The use of Roman numerals continued until 1800 when Arabic numerals became popular. Today, both styles are used.

Grandfather clocks made by Nathaniel Mulliken used the elaborately engraved brass dials. Because it is just about impossible to make a brass dial today like the beautiful dials he made, a painted dial has been substituted and illustrated in this book. Occasionally, an original dial face can be found at an auction or flea market.

Tools Needed to Build This Clock

This clock requires very few tools to build. The average woodshop should have most of these. Basic hand tools will be required along with the following power tools:

☐ Table saw or radial arm saw
☐ Router and/or shaper
☐ Jig saw or sabre saw
☐ Lathe
☐ Sander
☐ Planer (optional, but handy)

Materials List

The materials list is a list giving the *overall* sizes of each part needed to build one grandfather clock per the given plans (Illus. D). It includes how many of each part is required and if the part is to be made of primary

NO.	NAME OF PART	MAT'L Primary Secondary	THICK	WIDTH	LG.	RQ'D
1	BACKBOARD	S	5/8	14 1/2	84 3/16	1
2	SIDE	P	3/4	6 5/8	63 13/16	2
3	BOTTOM	S	3/4	7 -	14 1/2	1
4	BRACE	S	3/4	- 3/4	61 -	2
5	FRONT STILES	P	3/4	2 3/4	61 1/16	2
6	BOTTOM RAIL	P	3/4	4 -	11 3/4	1
7	TOP RAIL	P	3/4	8 -	11 3/4	1
10	LARGE FILLER	S	1/2	5 -	40 -	1
11	SMALL FILLER	S	1/2	1 1/2	40 -	1
12	BASE MATERIAL	P	3/4	13 1/2	40 -	1
16	BACK SUPPORT	S	3/4	2 3/4	14 1/2	1
17	BASE MOLDING	P	1 1/8	2 1/4	48 -	1
18	WAIST MOLDING	P	1 3/8	2 1/4	90 -	1
23	OUTSIDE BOTTOM MOLDING	P	5/8	4 1/4	40 -	1
26	HOOD SHIM	S	1/8	1 -	7 -	2
27	DOOR	P	3/4	9 1/2	43 1/16	1
29	BASE FRONT	P	5/8	1 5/8	17 3/8	1
30	BASE SIDE	P	5/8	1 5/16	7 1/2	1
31	HOOD MOLDING	P	5/8	- 3/4	48 -	1
34	SIDE PANEL	P	3/8	7 1/16	23 1/16	2
35	TOE BOARD	S	3/4	7 7/16	15 7/16	1
37	COLUMN	P	1 3/16	1 3/16	16 1/4	4
38	LARGE FILLER	P	1/2	4 1/2	48 -	1
39	SMALL FILLER	S	1/2	1 1/2	48 -	1
40	HOOD MATERIAL	P	3/4	8 1/16	48 -	1
44	HOOD MOLDING	P	13/16	1 -	36 -	1
47	CENTER HOOD MOLDING	P	13/16	6 -	15 1/2	1
50	HOOD MOLDING	P	3/8	1 1/2	48 -	1
53	HOOD DOOR MOLDING	P	3/4	1 5/8	54 -	1
56	DOOR TOP	P	3/4	6 -	12 11/16	1
	DIAL FACE	S	1/4	13 1/2	18 1/2	1

Illus. D. List of materials.

wood (P) or secondary wood (S) such as pine or some other similarly inexpensive wood. Most parts will require some work to shape or mold them to exact specifications per the drawings.

Note: the original grandfather clock by Nathaniel was made of maple wood with a very light stain, as most of his clocks were. The copy illustrated is made of cherry wood and no stain was used. It is recommended that most any hardwood be used but that pine wood *not* be used for the primary parts as it is very soft, does not have a nice wood pattern for a clock, and does not finish as well as a hardwood does.

Using the Drawings in This Text

At the end of Section III, a two-view drawing is provided for each part. One view is the FRONT VIEW and the other is either the RIGHT-SIDE VIEW or the TOP VIEW. The views are positioned in a standard way exactly as they are in industry. The front view is always the most important view and the starting place for studying the drawings. The right-side view is always located directly to the right of the front view; the top view is always located directly above the front view.

Dash lines indicate hidden surfaces or features within the object. Think of these lines as X-rays showing what the inside will look like. At times, a SECTION VIEW is used to further illustrate a particular feature of the project. The section view is a partial view that illustrates only a portion of the project such as the detail or shape of a molding. Each important step of the assembly has an *exploded view* that illustrates how the clock is to be put together. It is important that you fully understand how the clock is to be assembled before any work is started.

The drawings or plans are referenced as ''figures'' in the text of section III. In addition to these, there are illustrations and photos to help you better visualize each step.

Section III

CONSTRUCTING THE CLOCK

Constructing
the Clock

BECAUSE EACH READER IS AT A DIFFERENT LEVEL OF WOODWORKING SKILL and will have totally different woodworking equipment, I have given only general overall instructions for each part. Those lacking in one or more larger pieces of equipment such as a shaper or lathe may wish to enroll in an evening adult woodworking class to develop the few parts requiring special woodworking equipment.

As with any project, it is important that you fully understand how the clock case and hood is to be assembled. A good idea is to study the assembly and parts drawings *at the end of this section* before you begin. Figures 1 through 28 refer to building the case; Figs. 29 through 61 refer to building the hood. The numbers of the figures also correspond with the parts numbers on the materials list in the last section (Illus. D) as well as the numbers within the figures themselves. Also, it is very important that all parts be cut to exact size and that square cuts are made. A good practice is to always dry-fit the parts before applying any glue.

Building the Case

All attempts have been made to check and recheck the many dimensions given in this book. At least eight clocks have been made to date using these plans; therefore, I hope any and all errors have been corrected. I still recommend that all dimensions be rechecked again as you proceed in building this clock.

STEP 1.

Study the subassembly drawing (Fig. no. 9) and be sure you understand how parts one through seven are assembled to form the case.

STEP 2.

Cut the back (Fig. no. 1) from a piece of pine or any secondary wood. Notch it as illustrated.

STEP 3.

Cut the two sides (Fig. no. 2) to size and cut the ⅜-inch × ¾-inch rabbet as shown. Cut the notch as shown making sure you cut a r.h. and l.h. (right-hand and left-hand) pair.

STEP 4.

The bottom (Fig. no. 3) is cut from pine also. Keep all cuts square.

STEP 5.

The two braces (Fig. no. 4) are also cut from scrap pine.

STEP 6.

Cut the front stile (Fig. no. 5) to exact size and cut the ⅜-inch × ¾-inch rabbet. Locate and cut the three mortises as dimensioned, taking care to make a r.h. and l.h. pair.

STEP 7.

Cut to size the bottom rail (Fig. no. 6) and the top rail (Fig. no. 7) as dimensioned, and cut the tenons keeping sharp edges. It is important to maintain the 9-inch dimension on both parts and be square.

STEP 8.

Dry-fit the front stile (no. 5) to the bottom and top rails (nos. 6 and 7). Glue and clamp together, keeping the subassembly square (Fig. no. 8)

Cut sharp corners or shoulder for the tenons in the bottom and top rails. Note the mortise cuts in the front rails.

STEP 9.

Notch for the two hinges as shown. Use the actual hinges as patterns to ensure a good, tight fit. Note that the notch is cut at 15 degrees.

STEP 10.

Locate and drill the eight ¼-inch diameter holes and add ¼-inch × ¾-inch long dowels. Sand all over.

STEP 11.

Refer to Fig. no. 9 and dry-fit the case together as shown. Glue the back board (no. 1), the two sides (no. 2), the bottom (no. 3), and the front subassembly (Fig. no. 8) together. Clamp as required. Add the two braces (no. 4). Glue and nail into place. Double-check that everything is square and that the ends all line up.

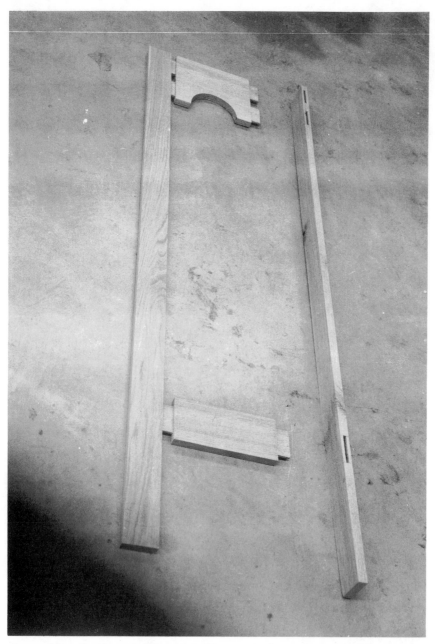

Assembly of subassembly no. 8. Be sure to keep the assembly square.

STEP 12.

Sand all over keeping all edges very sharp.

Gluing and clamping the backboard with the two sides.

STEP 13.

Cut to size the large and small fillers (Fig. nos. 10 and 11).

Check for proper fit before gluing into place.

Adding subassembly no. 8 to the backboard and sides.

STEP 14.

Cut to size the base material (Fig. no. 12). Glue material together if necessary to obtain the 13½-inch width.

Gluing and clamping subassembly no. 9. Check that the case is square.

Planing subassembly no. 8 to match with the two sides.

STEP 15.

Choose the best side of no. 12 and glue the large and small fillers (nos. 10 and 11) to the *back* side as shown in the subassembly (Fig. no. 13).

STEP 16.

Using Fig. no. 14, make the 45-degree cuts. Before cutting, check the inside 14½-inch dimension against the actual case. Be sure the cuts are at exactly 45 degrees and cut square across the board. *This is extremely important.* Cut the lower notch as dimensioned.

STEP 17.

Using the remaining base front subassembly no. 14, cut a r.h. and l.h. pair of the base side (Fig. no. 15). It is a good idea to cut them ¼-inch longer than required and trim off after assembly with case. Notch as illustrated for clearance of the feet. Add a ½-inch × 1-inch piece of scrapwood as shown.

STEP 18.

Check that the parts go together with the case and have good tight joints. Trim to fit if necessary.

STEP 19.

Cut the back support (Fig. no. 16) of pine as shown.

STEP 20.

The base and waist moldings (Fig. nos. 17 and 18) are made by making a *cove cut* using a table or radial-arm saw. This technique involves passing the stock by the saw blade at an *angle* instead of parallel to the blade. Depending on the angle, most anything from a wide circular cross section to an extremely narrow elliptical cove molding can be made.

The table saw must be set up as shown in Illus. E. At the end of the stock, sketch the desired profile. Adjust the blade to the depth of the cut and adjust the temporary fence to an angle that, when sighted from the end of the board, agrees with the desired profile. A little experimentation will have to be done to get it exactly correct. When correct, clamp the temporary fence at that angle. Reset the saw blade so it extends up approximately ¹⁄₁₆ inch. Pass the stock across the blade, then raise the blade another ¹⁄₁₆ inch. Repeat these steps until the required cove is achieved. It is a good idea to make smaller and smaller upward adjustments as the desired shape is achieved and to pass the material over the blade very slowly for the final cuts. A 60-tooth carbide-combination saw blade will produce a smooth cove cut.

The radial arm saw makes this job even easier, as the blade can simply be set at an angle and the stock fed into it using the regular fence. Make the cove cuts for the base and waist molding (nos. 17 and 18), as recommended above. Using a router or shaper, cut the remaining profile as illustrated.

STEP 21.

Cut the 45-degree angles in the front base molding and front waist

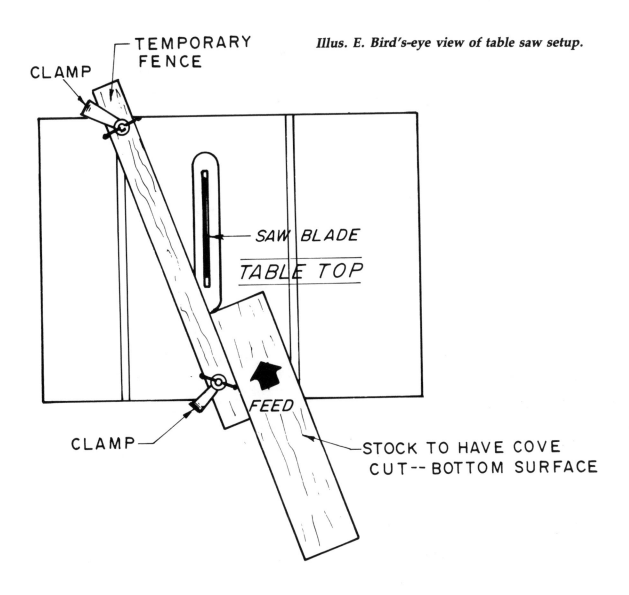

CLAMP

TEMPORARY FENCE

Illus. E. Bird's-eye view of table saw setup.

SAW BLADE

TABLE TOP

FEED

CLAMP

STOCK TO HAVE COVE CUT -- BOTTOM SURFACE

molding (Fig. nos. 19 and 20 from nos. 17 and 18), respectively. Be sure to recheck the 14½-inch dimension against the case *before* making this cut. Adjust if necessary.

STEP 22.

Cut the 45-degree angle in the side base molding and side waist molding (Fig. nos. 21 and 22). It is a good idea to add ¼-inch to the overall length and then trim it to exact length after assembly. Check for a good tight fit. Trim if necessary.

Cove-cutting the molding using a radial arm saw in place of a table saw.

STEP 23.

Cut to size the outside bottom molding (Fig. no. 23) and using a router or shaper cut the top shape as shown.

STEP 24.

From the outside bottom molding (no. 23) cut the outside bottom/front molding (Fig. no. 24). Again *before* cutting, check the 17-inch dimension against no. 14. After making the miter cuts, make a cardboard pattern of the left end using the given dimensions. Trace this pattern on the ends and cut to shape as shown.

STEP 25.

From the outside bottom molding (no. 23), cut a r.h. and l.h. pair of bottom/side moldings (Fig. no. 25), as shown. Cut the legs using the cardboard pattern.

Gluing and clamping moldings in place. Be sure to cut an exact 45-degree angle at the joint.

STEP 26.

Note how the hinges are attached to the door and side of the case (see Fig. no. 26). Ball and Ball number 17-065 is recommended as it is very close to the original clock. If a regular hinge with finials is used, one leaf will have to be extended about ½ inch as illustrated.

STEP 27.

Check the *exact* size of the door opening of your case. It should be about ¼ inch smaller on all sides than dimensions on the drawing. Adjust your door if required to fit your opening. After checking, cut the door to size and, using a shaper, cut the edges as illustrated in Fig. no. 27. A router could be used for this cut if necessary. Notch for the hinges by using the actual hinge and the case as a guide. Note, part of the ¼-inch-radius lip is actually cut away.

STEP 28.

Refer to Fig. no. 28, assembly and exploded view. Assemble the molding to the case as illustrated. Keep good tight joints. Fill and sand all over and set aside. This completes the clock case subassembly.

Building the Hood

The hood is more difficult to build than the case so extra care should be taken in all cuts and measurements. Check and recheck all measurements and cuts before making them. Be sure you fully understand *how* the hood is assembled before starting.

STEP 1.

Study the exploded view for the base subassembly (Fig. no. 33).

STEP 2.

Cut the base front (Fig. no. 29) to size and cut the two ¼-inch × ¾-inch mortises as shown.

STEP 3.

Cut to size the base side (Fig. no. 30) and cut the tenon and rabbet as shown—be sure to make a r.h. and l.h. pair.

STEP 4.

Cut to overall size the hood molding (Fig. no. 31). It is a good idea to make twice as much as actually required in case of an error later. Using a router or shaper, cut the profile as illustrated. If you do *not* have the cutter bits to make the exact profile, cut it as closely as possible to the illustrated profile with the cutter bits you do have.

STEP 5.

From the hood molding (no. 31), cut the front and side hood moldings (Fig. no. 32). Double-check the 17⅜-inch dimension against the base front (no. 30). Cut no. 32, ¼ inch longer and trim to exact size *after* assembling—don't forget to cut a r.h. and l.h. pair.

STEP 6.

Glue the base front (no. 29) to the base sides (no. 30), keeping it square. Add the front and side moldings (no. 32). Note the rabbet cuts in the base sides (no. 30) are *up* and that the front and side hood moldings (no. 32) are *flush* with the top surface, as shown in the exploded view of the subassembly (Fig. no. 33).

Subassembly no. 36. Note the ⅜-inch overhang of the top board.

STEP 7.

Study the subassembly and exploded view, (Fig. nos. 36-A and 36-B) so you fully understand how the hood goes together.

STEP 8.

Cut to size and make a r.h. and l.h. pair of the side panel (Fig. no. 34). Cut the notch as shown, then locate and cut the tombstone window opening. Using a router on the *back side*, route ¼-inch-deep ledge to support the glass, 4½ inches × 9¾ inches, leaving an ⅛-inch-thick material left. From the outside surface, round the edge as shown using a router or hand rasp. Sand all over.

STEP 9.

Out of pine, cut to size the top board (Fig. no. 35). Keep all cuts square as shown.

STEP 10.

Refer to the subassembly and exploded view (Figs. 36-A and 36-B). Dry-fit all parts to be sure everything fits correctly. Carefully locate and drill the four ⅜-inch-diameter holes, taking care not to tear through with the drill. Drill *in* from both surfaces.

STEP 11.

Turn the hood assembly upside down and locate and drill the four ⅜-inch-diameter holes so they will be spaced and in *exact* line with those drilled in step 10.

STEP 12.

Assemble the hood using nos. 33, 34, and 35. Take extra care to keep everything *square*. Note the ⅜-inch overhang in front of no. 35.

STEP 13.

Refer to the column (Fig. no. 37). There must be four columns *exactly* the same. If possible, use a finished column, or "copy-cat," attached to your lathe so they will be all the same. Important: so your square corners will not chip off when stepping down to the 1⅛-inch diameter, add masking tape over the two square areas (see shaded areas on Fig.). Note the 15½-

inch dimension must be exactly held to size. Sand the column all over *before* removing from the lathe.

STEP 14.

Cut to size, the large and small fillers (Fig. nos. 38 and 39), as shown. Note no. 38 is cut from primary wood and no. 39 is cut from pine.

STEP 15.

Cut to size the hood material (Fig. no. 40). As this will be seen, choose a nice piece of wood with a lot of "character."

Inside view of the hood subassembly (no. 41) with the large filler and small filler in place. The inside surface must match with subassembly no. 36.

STEP 16.

Choose the best side of no. 40 and glue the large and small fillers (nos. 38 and 39) to the *back* side as shown in the subassembly (Fig. 41).

STEP 17.

Using the subassembly (Fig. no. 41), make the 45-degree cuts as shown. *Before* making these cuts, double-check the 15⁷⁄₁₆-inch dimension against the actual hood subassembly (Fig. 36). Make the 45-degree cuts exact and make square cuts across the board. *This is important.* Cut the 7-inch arc as illustrated.

STEP 18.

Using the remaining subassembly (no. 41), cut a r.h. and l.h. pair of the hood side (no. 43). Again, it is a good idea to add ¼ inch to the overall length and trim *after* assembly with hood. Add a piece of scrap wood ½-inch × 1-inch as shown.

STEP 19.

Check that the parts go together with the hood, that they remain parallel and square, and that they form a good tight joint.

STEP 20.

Adding the four columns (no. 37), attach the hood front and sides (nos. 42 and 43) to the hood subassembly. Make sure you have good corner joints and that everything is square.

STEP 21.

Cut to size the hood molding (Fig. no. 44). Again, it is recommended that you cut twice as much as you need in case of an error later. Using either a router or shaper, cut the profile as shown. Use whatever cutter bits you have and come as close as possible to the profile shown. Important: with the same cutter bits and same settings, cut out the inside curve of the center hood molding (Fig. no. 47). Note, *after* the inside curve has been cut to profile, cut the top, 8-inch radius. Cut the ends at 60 degrees as shown *after* checking with the actual hood. Make this cut *last* and only after checking with the hood assembly. This arch must fit tightly with the two hood molding front pieces (Fig. no. 46).

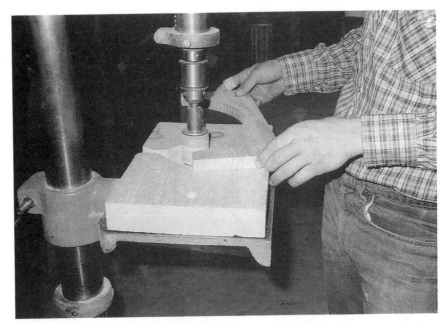

Sawing the inside surface of the center hood molding. Cut the outside surface last after the molding has been cut.

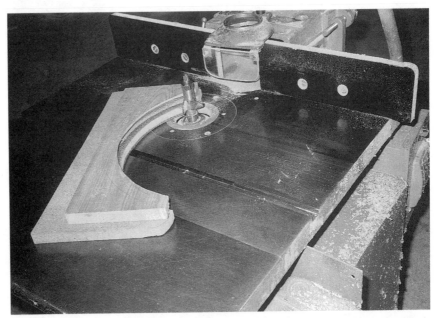

Using a shaper or router, cut the profile of the center hood molding. Add the molding to the hood assembly (no. 41).

STEP 22.

From the hood molding (no. 44), cut the front and side moldings (nos. 45 and 46). Note: the given dimensions are very close in size but it is a good idea to hand fit each part on the hood assembly as you go.

Glue and clamp, keeping all corners square.

Inside view of basic hood subassembly.

STEP 23.

Start with the center molding (no. 47) and work out and around the sides from there. Dry-fit the moldings. When correct, glue and nail the molding in place. Keep good, tight joints as you go. Use the given dimensions and angles as a guide only. Fit the molding to *your* hood. Use small square-cut nails and do not try to hide them.

Front view of basic hood subassembly, minus hood moldings.

STEP 24.

Cut the hood moldings (Fig. nos. 48 and 49) from no. 17 and fit them to the hood assembly. Note: These parts are located ⅜ inch from the top surface. The ⅜-inch space is for the top hood moldings (nos. 51 and 52).

STEP 25.

Cut to size the top molding (Fig. no. 50) and "round" on edge as per the drawing.

STEP 26.

From the top molding (no. 50), cut and fit the final hood moldings (Fig. nos. 51 and 52).

STEP 27.

Fill and sand all over, keeping all edges sharp and square. This completes the hood subassembly. The only thing left is making and adding the door.

STEP 28.

Cut to size and shape the hood door molding (Fig. no. 53). Again, it is a good idea to cut twice as much material as you think you will actually need in the event of an error. Important: while cutting the bead and rabbet for the glass, cut the interior arc of the door top (no. 56) with the same cutting bit and settings.

STEP 29.

From the hood door molding (no. 53), cut the two door stiles (Fig. no. 54). Carefully cut away the bead at 45 degrees as shown. The 1⅜ inch is crucial. Locate and cut the two ¼ inch × 1 inch mortises per given dimensions.

STEP 30.

From the hood door molding (no. 53), cut the door base according to Fig. no. 55. Cut the two tenons and cut 45 degrees from the bead as shown.

STEP 31.

Complete making the door top (no. 56) and carefully cut the two mortises as illustrated.

STEP 32.

Dry-fit the door parts per Fig. no. 58 and adjust if necessary. If they fit correctly, glue the door together, keeping all corners square. Fill and sand all over, keeping all edges sharp.

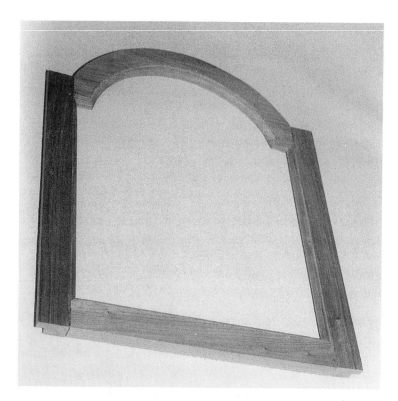

Door subassembly no. 58. Check for a good fit with subassembly no. 60.

Escutcheon plate from the original clock.

STEP 33.

At this time, lay out and cut from a piece of ¹⁄₁₆-inch-thick brass the two hinges per the drawing. Polish the brass with a buffing wheel to obtain a bright brass finish. From two other pieces of ¹⁄₁₆-inch-thick brass, cut to size, the two escutcheons (Fig. no. 59). This is easier than it looks. Start with the various center openings by drilling holes as illustrated and file the shape using a small file. *Note:* Ball and Ball make a very nice hinge [# H28-251], that could be used in the place of part no. 57. Their escutcheon plates [# L101-056 and # L101-057] *could* be used in place of no.

Second escutcheon plate from the original clock.

59—although this is not exactly authentic. It is best to file the exact shapes of no. 59. This will give you a greater sense of accomplishment.

STEP 34.

Carefully locate and mortise the *left* door stile to fit your door lock. At this time, temporarily add (for fit only) the hinge and second escutcheon. They will have to be removed for finishing. *Note:* the right door stile must be notched for the hinge (no. 57) at the top and bottom edge.

STEP 35.

With the door hinges (no. 57) screwed to the door at the top and bottom, fit and attach the door to the hood with two ⅝-inch-long brass brads, nailing through the holes in the hinge ear. Check that the door opens and clears correctly. Trim to fit if necessary. Mortise the case front stile (no. 5) for the lock. Also, check that the hood door lock functions and locks correctly.

STEP 36.

Go back to the clock *case* and carefully locate and mortise the *left* side of the case door (no. 27) to fit your door lock. Also, temporarily add (for fit only) the first escutcheon (no. 59-A) and your door lock. Check that the door lock functions and locks correctly.

STEP 37.

Lay out and cut to size the dial blank (Fig. no. 61) from ³⁄₁₆-inch thick material. Using oil-base paint, prime and paint it on *both* sides so it will not warp because of moisture getting into the back surface. Sand between coats so there is a smooth surface and give the dial face a final off-white final coat. Allow to dry for 48 hours or more before applying the numbers to the face.

STEP 38.

Check that the hood slides over and into the clock case. Trim to fit if necessary.

STEP 39.

Using the inside opening of the door, make a cardboard pattern for the glass. Check that your cardboard pattern fits into the opening correctly and have a piece of glass cut to size. You may have to "round" the glass

Note the small latch used to hold the hood assembly in place.

slightly where the arch intersects the straight top edge of the glass. Insert the glass into the door after finishing the hood with black putty.

STEP 40.

Cut two pieces of glass for the side windows about 4¼-inches × 9¼-inches and putty in place with black putty. This completes the hood subassembly.

SIDE VIEW

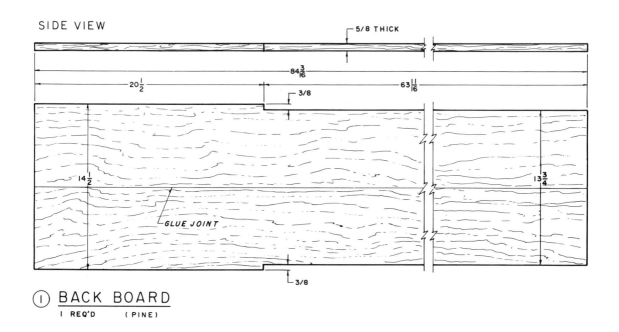

5/8 THICK

84 3/16

20 1/2

63 11/16

3/8

14 1/2

GLUE JOINT

13 3/4

3/8

① BACK BOARD

1 REQ'D   (PINE)

SIDE VIEW

FRONT VIEW

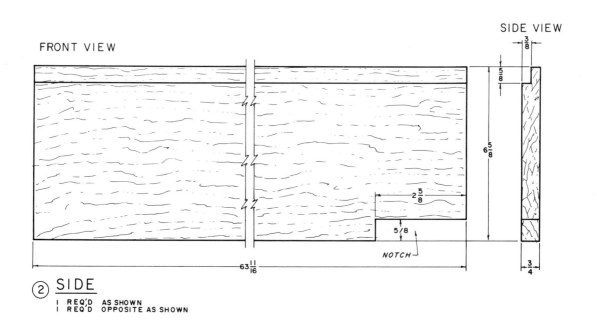

3/8

5/8

6 5/8

2 5/8

5/8

NOTCH

3/4

63 11/16

② SIDE

1 REQ'D   AS SHOWN
1 REQ'D   OPPOSITE AS SHOWN

FRONT VIEW
SIDE VIEW

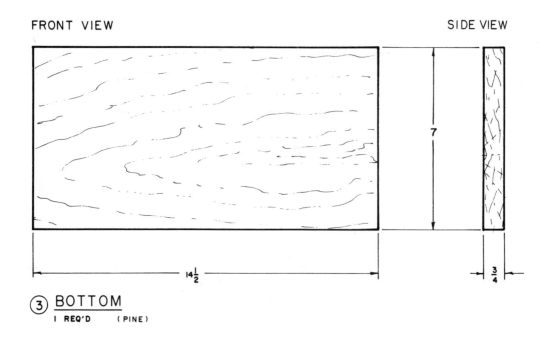

$14\frac{1}{2}$

7

$\frac{3}{4}$

③ BOTTOM
I REQ'D   (PINE)

FRONT VIEW
SIDE VIEW

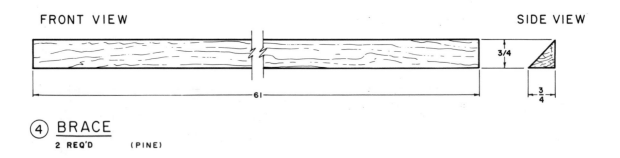

61

3/4

$\frac{3}{4}$

④ BRACE
2 REQ'D   (PINE)

TOP VIEW

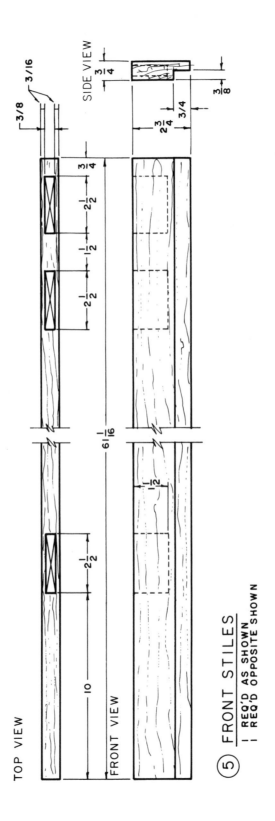

FRONT VIEW

SIDE VIEW

⑤ FRONT STILES
1 REQ'D AS SHOWN
1 REQ'D OPPOSITE SHOWN

49

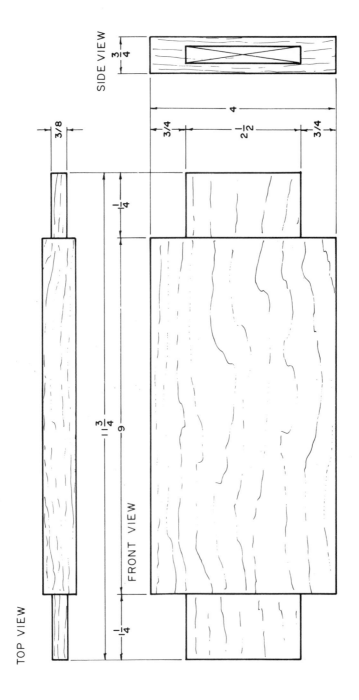

SIDE VIEW

$\frac{3}{4}$

TOP VIEW

FRONT VIEW

$3/8$

$3/4$

$2\frac{1}{2}$

$3/4$

4

$1\frac{1}{4}$

$11\frac{3}{4}$

9

$1\frac{1}{4}$

⑥ BOTTOM RAIL

1 REQ'D

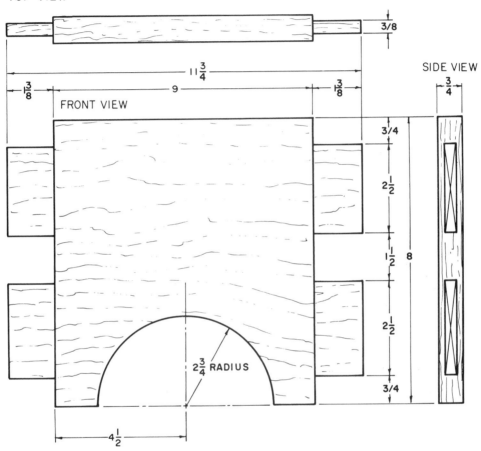

TOP VIEW

FRONT VIEW

SIDE VIEW

$11\frac{3}{4}$

9

$\frac{3}{8}$

$1\frac{3}{8}$

3/8

$\frac{3}{4}$

3/4

$2\frac{1}{2}$

$1\frac{1}{2}$

$2\frac{1}{2}$

3/4

8

$2\frac{3}{4}$ RADIUS

$4\frac{1}{2}$

⑦ TOP RAIL
I REQ'D

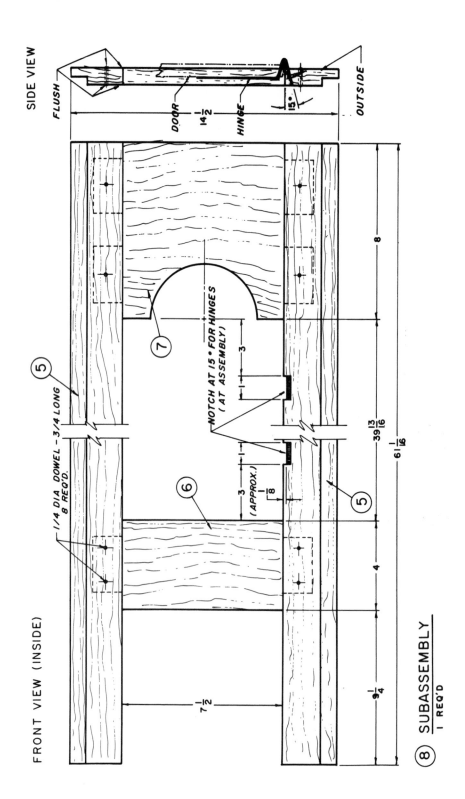

SIDE VIEW

FLUSH

DOOR

$14\frac{1}{2}$

HINGE

15°

OUTSIDE

FRONT VIEW (INSIDE)

1/4 DIA DOWEL - 3/4 LONG
8 REQ'D.

NOTCH AT 15° FOR HINGES
(AT ASSEMBLY)

5

7

6

5

3

1

3
(APPROX.)

$1\frac{1}{8}$

8

$39\frac{13}{16}$

$61\frac{1}{16}$

4

$9\frac{1}{4}$

$7\frac{1}{2}$

8   SUBASSEMBLY
1 REQ'D

FRONT VIEW   SIDE VIEW

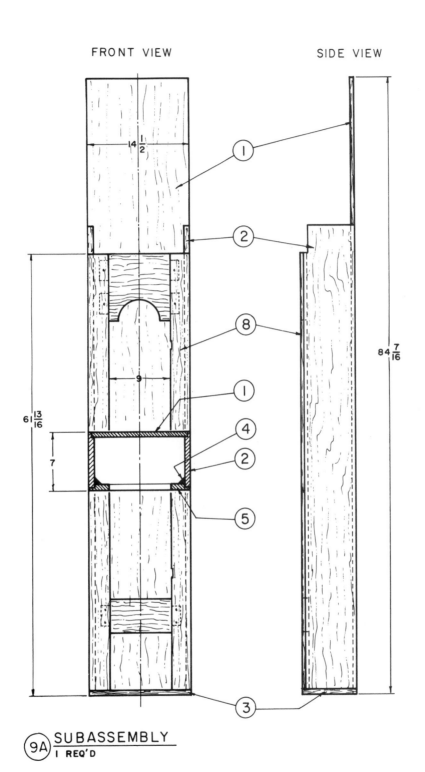

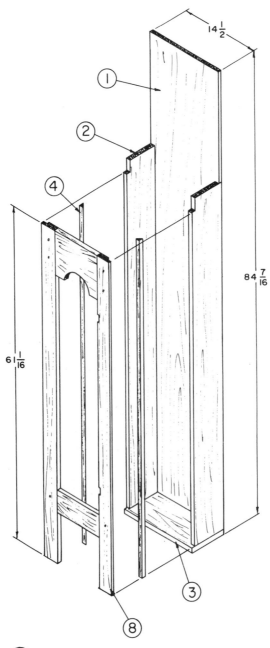

①

②

④

$14\frac{1}{2}$

$84\frac{7}{16}$

$61\frac{1}{16}$

③

⑧

⑨B EXPLODED VIEW
1 REQ'D

54

FRONT VIEW   SIDE VIEW

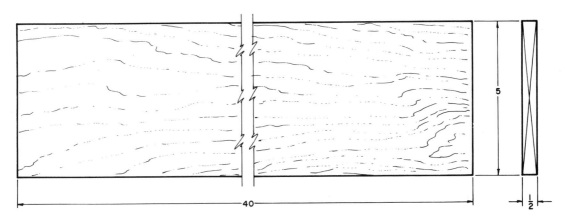

5

40 $\frac{1}{2}$

(10) LARGE FILLER
    1 REQ'D   (PINE)

FRONT VIEW   SIDE VIEW

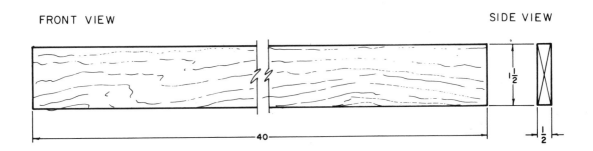

$1\frac{1}{2}$

40 $\frac{1}{2}$

(11) SMALL FILLER
    1 REQ'D   (PINE)

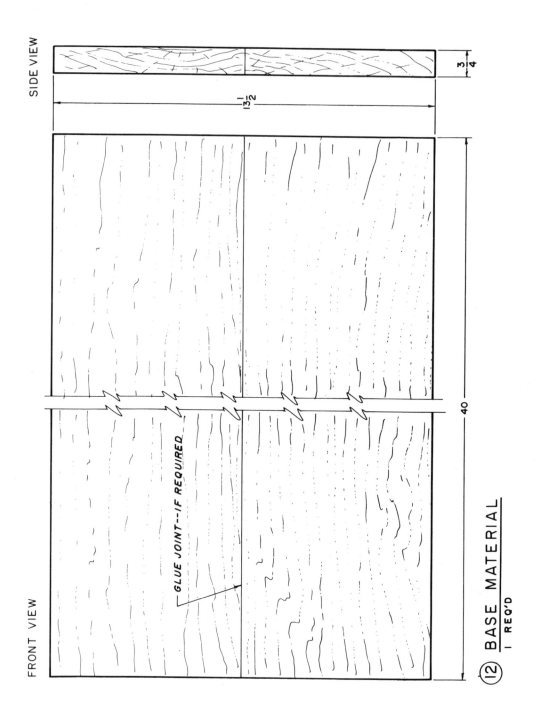

SIDE VIEW

$13\frac{1}{2}$

$\frac{3}{4}$

FRONT VIEW

GLUE JOINT--IF REQUIRED

40

⑫ BASE MATERIAL
1 REQ'D

SIDE VIEW

GLUE IN PLACE

⑫

⑪

⑩

FRONT VIEW

⑫

⑬ SUB ASSEMBLY
I REQ'D

57

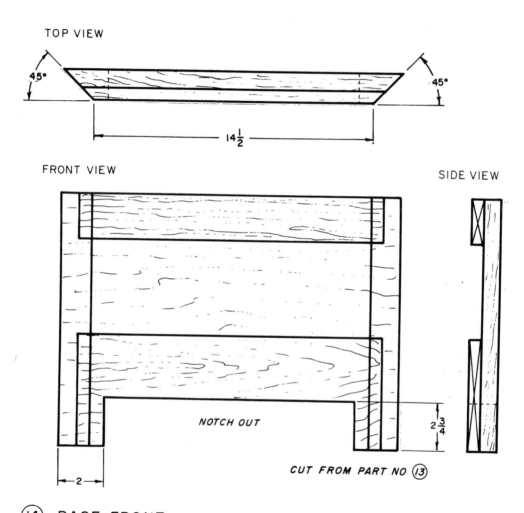

TOP VIEW

45°   45°

14½

FRONT VIEW   SIDE VIEW

NOTCH OUT

CUT FROM PART NO ⑬

2¾

2

⑭ BASE FRONT
1 REQ'D

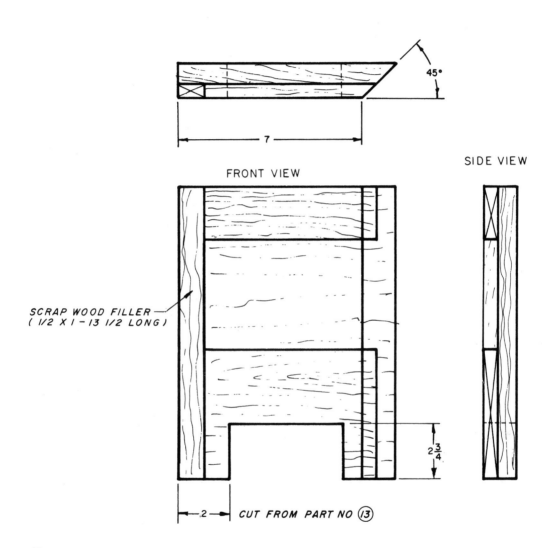

45°

7

FRONT VIEW

SIDE VIEW

SCRAP WOOD FILLER
(1/2 X 1 - 13 1/2 LONG)

$2\frac{3}{4}$

.2   CUT FROM PART NO ⑬

⑮ BASE SIDE
     1 REQ'D AS SHOWN
     1 REQ'D OPPOSITE SHOWN

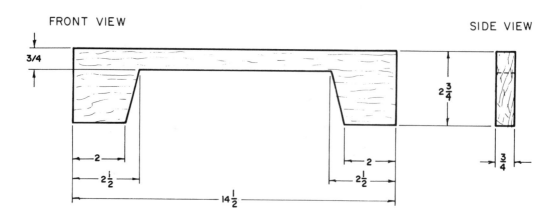

FRONT VIEW

SIDE VIEW

3/4

2 3/4

3/4

2

2 1/2

2

2 1/2

14 1/2

(16) BACK SUPPORT

1 REQ'D (PINE)

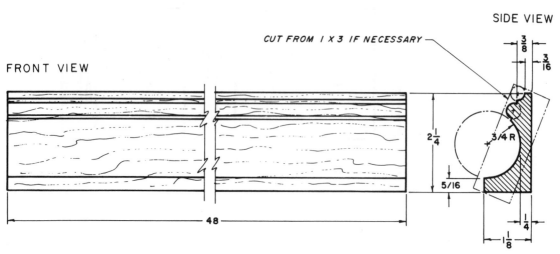

SIDE VIEW

CUT FROM 1 X 3 IF NECESSARY

3/8

3/16

FRONT VIEW

2 1/4

3/4 R

5/16

48

1/4

1/8

(17) BASE MOLDING

1 REQ'D

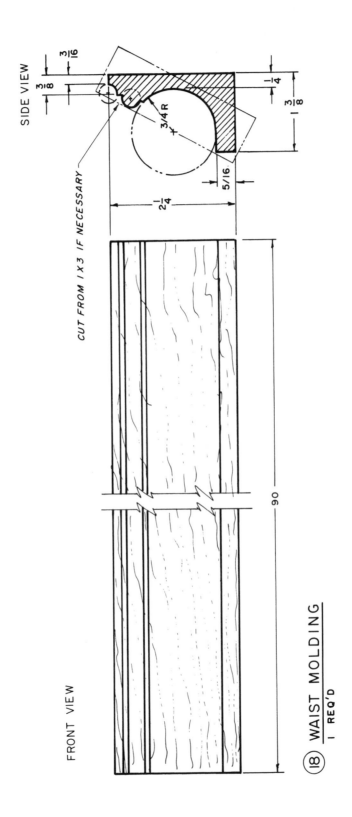

SIDE VIEW

$\frac{3}{16}$

$\frac{3}{8}$

$\frac{1}{4}$

$\frac{3}{8}$

$1\frac{3}{8}$

3/4 R

5/16

$2\frac{1}{4}$

CUT FROM 1 X 3 IF NECESSARY

FRONT VIEW

90

⑱ WAIST MOLDING
I REQ'D

61

SIDE VIEW

TOP VIEW

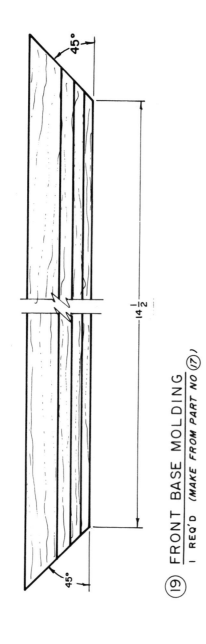

45°

45°

$14\frac{1}{2}$

⑲ FRONT BASE MOLDING

I REQ'D (MAKE FROM PART NO ⑰)

FRONT VIEW

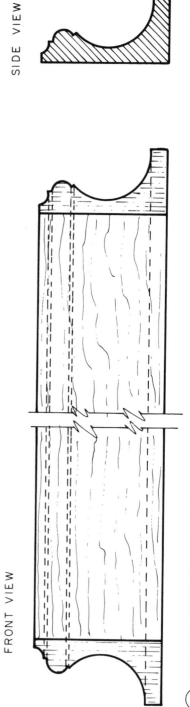

⑳ FRONT WAIST MOLDING

I REQ'D (MAKE FROM PART NO ⑱)

TOP VIEW

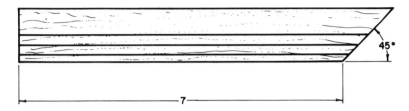

45°

7

(21) SIDE BASE MOLDING
1 REQ'D AS SHOWN
1 REQ'D OPPOSITE SHOWN }(MAKE FROM PART NO. (17))

FRONT VIEW

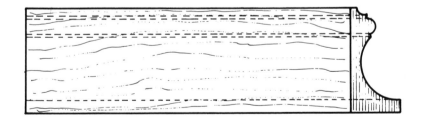

SIDE VIEW

(22) SIDE WAIST MOLDING
1 REQ'D AS SHOWN
1 REQ'D OPPOSITE SHOWN }(MAKE FROM PART NO. (18))

SIDE VIEW

1/8

1/8

3/4

4 1/4

5/8

FRONT VIEW

40

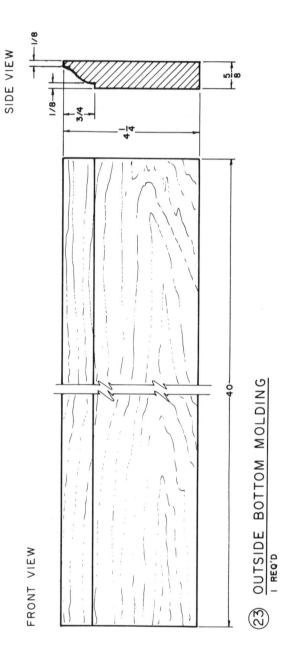

(23) OUTSIDE BOTTOM MOLDING

I REQ'D

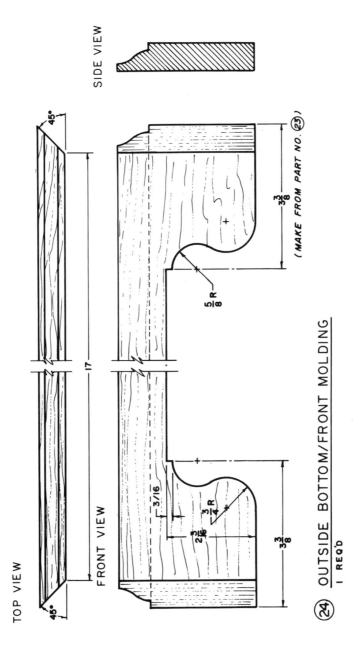

SIDE VIEW

TOP VIEW

FRONT VIEW

45°

45°

17

$3\frac{3}{8}$

$\frac{5}{8}$ R

(MAKE FROM PART NO. 23)

3/16

$2\frac{5}{16}$

$\frac{3}{4}$ R

$3\frac{3}{8}$

24 OUTSIDE BOTTOM/FRONT MOLDING
1 REQ'D

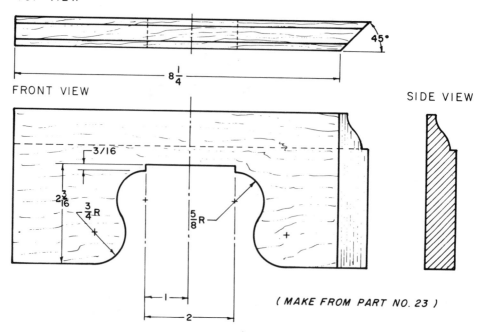

TOP VIEW

FRONT VIEW

SIDE VIEW

$8\frac{1}{4}$

45°

3/16

$2\frac{3}{16}$

$\frac{3}{4}$R

$\frac{5}{8}$R

1

2

(MAKE FROM PART NO. 23)

㉕ BOTTOM/SIDE MOLDING
1 REQ'D AS SHOWN
1 REQ'D OPPOSITE SHOWN

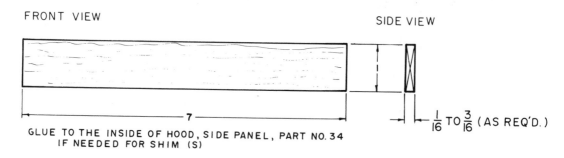

FRONT VIEW

SIDE VIEW

7

$\frac{1}{16}$ TO $\frac{3}{16}$ (AS REQ'D.)

GLUE TO THE INSIDE OF HOOD, SIDE PANEL, PART NO. 34
IF NEEDED FOR SHIM (S)

㉖ HOOD SHIM (IF REQ'D.)
2 REQ'D   (PINE)

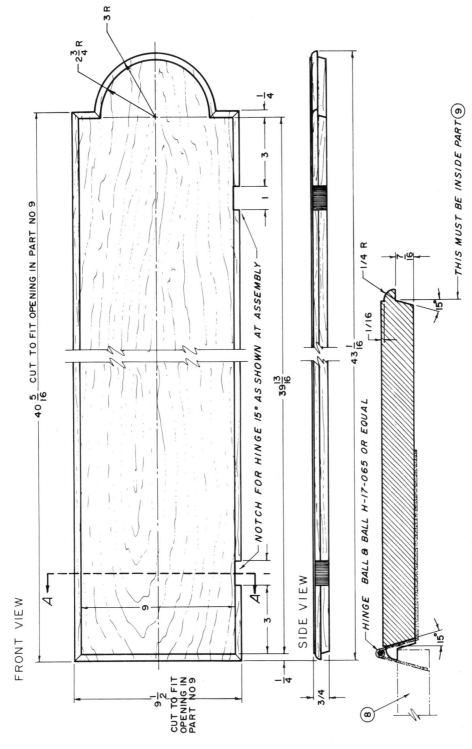

FRONT VIEW

CUT TO FIT OPENING IN PART NO 9

$40\frac{5}{16}$

$2\frac{3}{4}$ R

3 R

$\frac{1}{4}$

3

1

$39\frac{13}{16}$

NOTCH FOR HINGE 15° AS SHOWN AT ASSEMBLY

9

$9\frac{1}{2}$

CUT TO FIT OPENING IN PART NO 9

3

$\frac{1}{4}$

SIDE VIEW

$\frac{1}{4}$

3/4

HINGE BALL & BALL H-17-065 OR EQUAL

1/4 R

$\frac{7}{16}$

15°

$43\frac{1}{16}$

1/16

THIS MUST BE INSIDE PART 9

15°

8

VIEW LOOKING AT A-A

27 DOOR
I REQ'D

67

FRONT VIEW　　　　SIDE VIEW

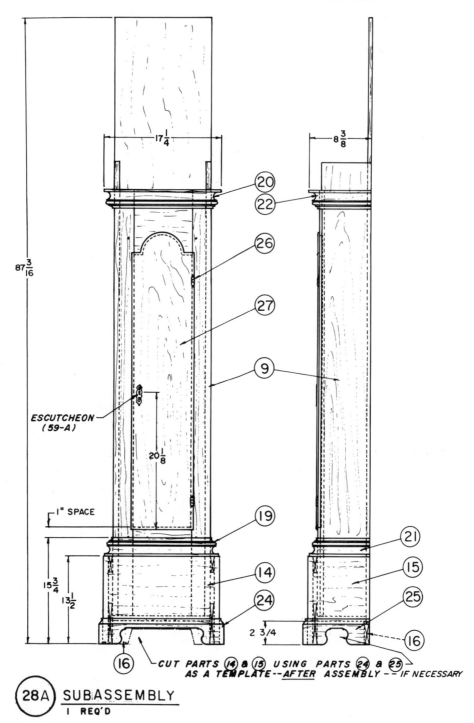

$17\frac{1}{4}$

$8\frac{3}{8}$

20
22
26
27
9

$87\frac{3}{16}$

ESCUTCHEON
(59-A)

$20\frac{1}{8}$

1" SPACE

19
21
14
15
24
25
16

$15\frac{3}{4}$
$13\frac{1}{2}$

2 3/4

16

CUT PARTS ⑭ & ⑮ USING PARTS ㉔ & ㉕
AS A TEMPLATE -- *AFTER* ASSEMBLY -- *IF NECESSARY*

(28A) SUBASSEMBLY
1 REQ'D

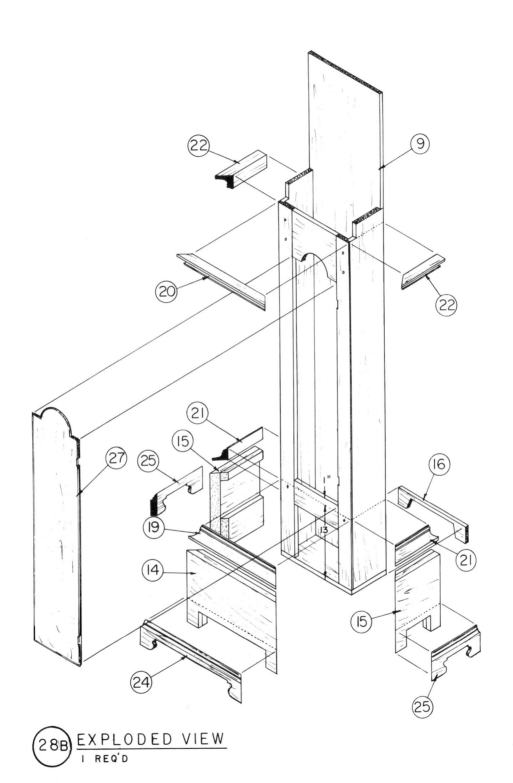

22 9

20

22

21
15
25
27
16
19
14
21
15
24
25

28B EXPLODED VIEW
I REQ'D

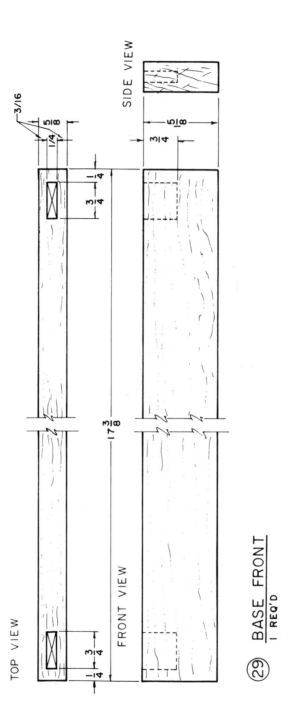

TOP VIEW

3/16

5/8

1/4

1/4

3/4

17 3/8

FRONT VIEW

3/4

1/4

SIDE VIEW

5/8

3/4

(29) BASE FRONT
1 REQ'D

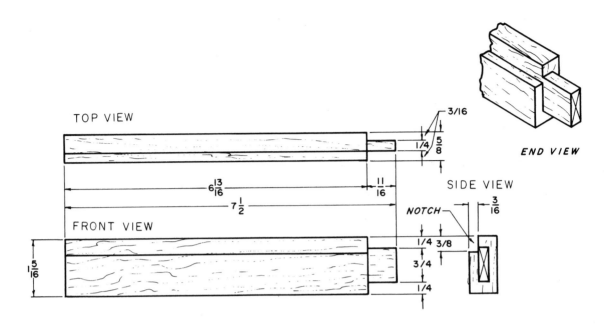

TOP VIEW

3/16

1/4 5/8

6 13/16

11/16

7 1/2

END VIEW

SIDE VIEW

FRONT VIEW

NOTCH

3/16

1 5/16

1/4 3/8

3/4

1/4

30 BASE SIDE
I REQ'D AS SHOWN
I REQ'D OPPOSITE SHOWN

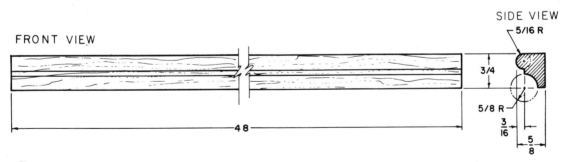

FRONT VIEW

SIDE VIEW
5/16 R

3/4

48

5/8 R

3/16

5/8

31 HOOD MOLDING
I REQ'D

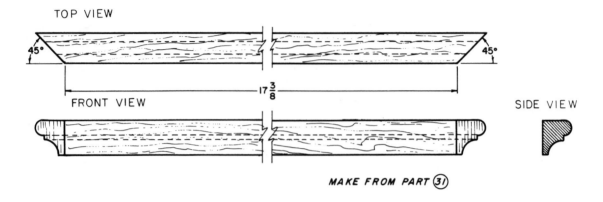

TOP VIEW

45° 45°

17 3/8

FRONT VIEW

SIDE VIEW

MAKE FROM PART ③

a. <u>FRONT HOOD MOLDING</u>
1 REQ'D

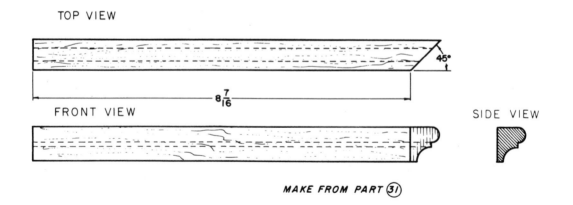

TOP VIEW

45°

8 7/16

FRONT VIEW

SIDE VIEW

MAKE FROM PART ③

b. <u>SIDE HOOD MOLDING</u>
1 REQ'D AS SHOWN
1 REQ'D OPPOSITE SHOWN

③② HOOD MOLDINGS

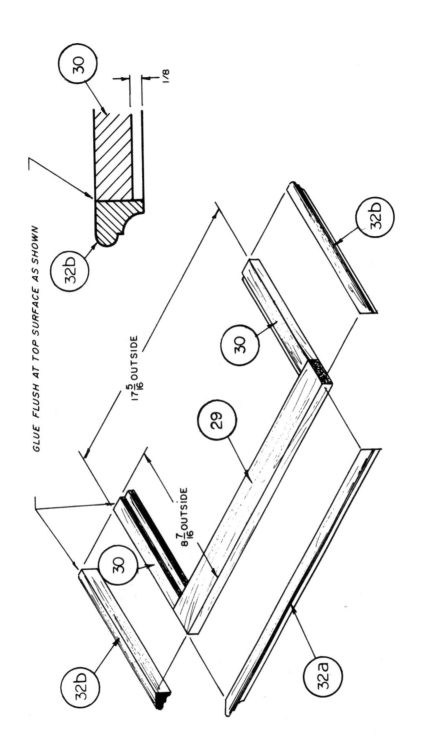

1/8

30

GLUE FLUSH AT TOP SURFACE AS SHOWN

32b

32b

30

29

$17\frac{5}{16}$ OUTSIDE

$8\frac{7}{16}$ OUTSIDE

32b

30

32a

33 SUBASSEMBLY
I REQ'D

73

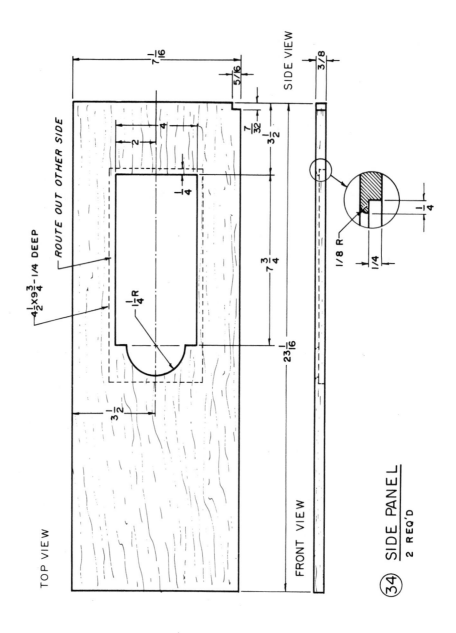

TOP VIEW

ROUTE OUT OTHER SIDE

$4\frac{1}{2} \times 9\frac{3}{4}$ – 1/4 DEEP

$7\frac{1}{16}$

$5/16$

$\frac{7}{32}$

4

2

$\frac{1}{4}$

$3\frac{1}{2}$

$\frac{1}{4}$ R

$7\frac{3}{4}$

$3\frac{1}{2}$

$23\frac{1}{16}$

FRONT VIEW

SIDE VIEW

$3/8$

$1/8$ R

$\frac{1}{4}$

$1/4$

34 SIDE PANEL
2 REQ'D

74

SIDE VIEW

$\frac{3}{4}$

$7\frac{7}{16}$

FRONT VIEW

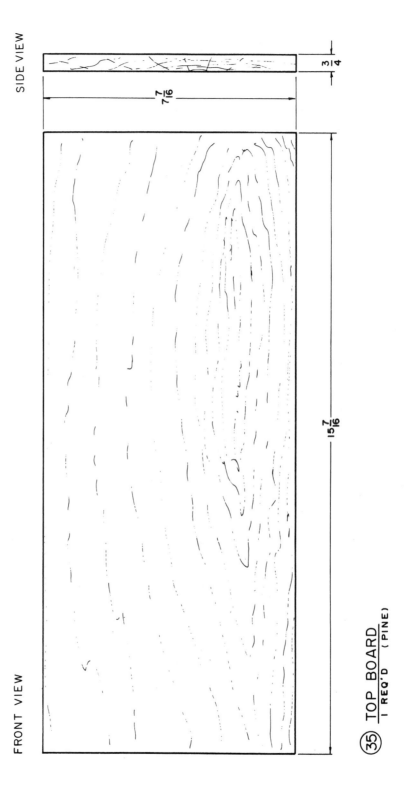

$15\frac{7}{16}$

(35) <u>TOP BOARD</u>
<u>I REQ'D (PINE)</u>

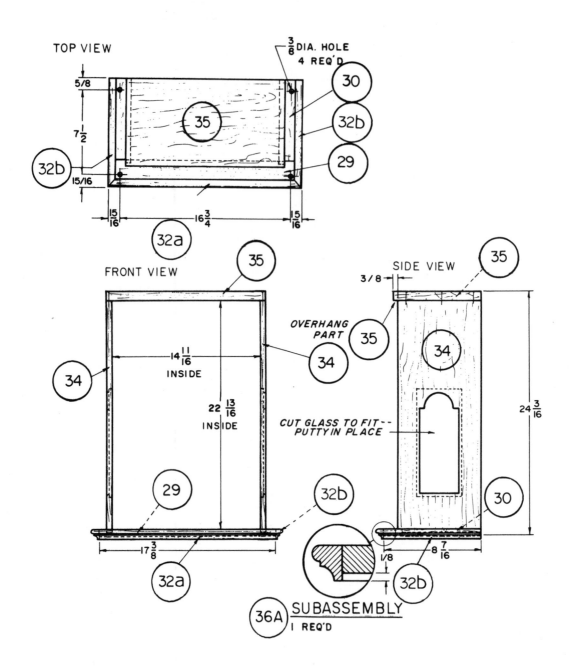

TOP VIEW

3/8 DIA. HOLE
4 REQ'D

30
32b
29

5/8
7 1/2
15/16

15/16   16 3/4   15/16

32a

FRONT VIEW

35

OVERHANG
PART

34

SIDE VIEW

35

35

34

14 11/16
INSIDE

34

22 13/16
INSIDE

3/8

CUT GLASS TO FIT --
PUTTY IN PLACE

24 3/16

29

32b

30

17 3/8

32a

32b

1/8

32b

8 7/16

36A SUBASSEMBLY
     I REQ'D

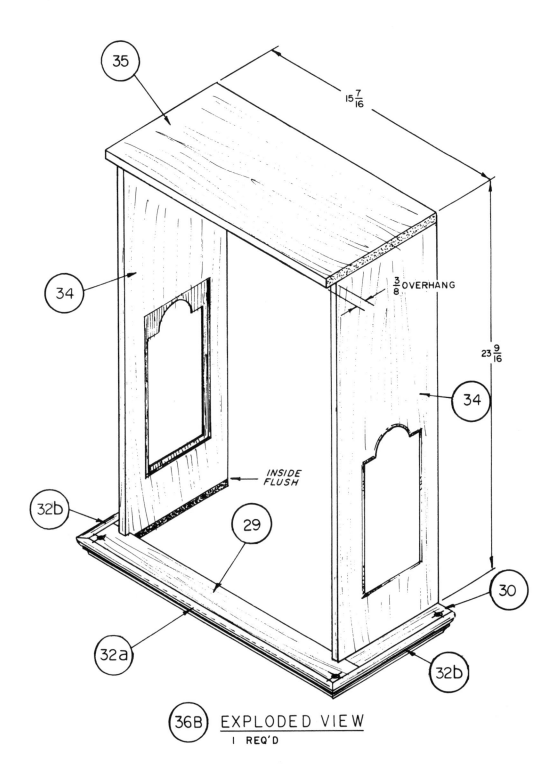

35

15 $\frac{7}{16}$

34

$\frac{3}{8}$ OVERHANG

23 $\frac{9}{16}$

34

INSIDE FLUSH

32b

29

30

32a

32b

36B EXPLODED VIEW
I REQ'D

77

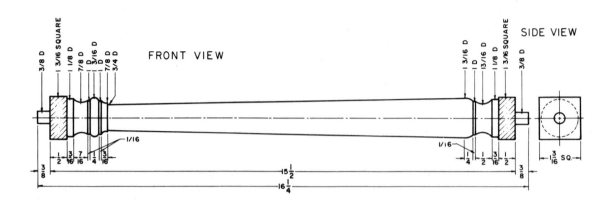

FRONT VIEW

SIDE VIEW

3/8 D
1 3/16 SQUARE
1 1/8 D
7/8 D
D
3/16 D
7/8 D
3/4 D

1 3/16 D
1 D
13/16 D
1 1/8 D
1 3/16 SQUARE
3/8 D

1/16

1/16

1/2 3/16 7/16 1/4 3/16 1/2

1 1/4 1/2 3/16 1/2

3/16 SQ.

3/8

15 1/2

16 1/4

3/8

(37) COLUMN
4 REQ'D

FRONT VIEW

SIDE VIEW

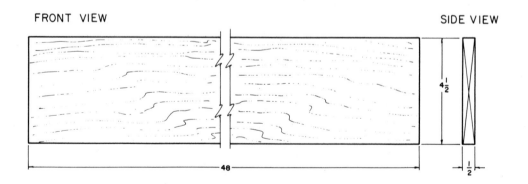

4 1/2

48

1/2

(38) LARGE FILLER
1 REQ'D

FRONT VIEW

SIDE VIEW

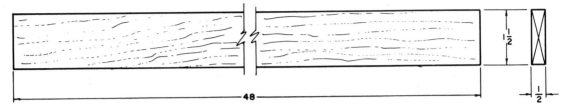

$1\frac{1}{2}$

48

$\frac{1}{2}$

(39) <u>SMALL FILLER</u>
I REQ'D   (PINE)

FRONT VIEW

SIDE VIEW

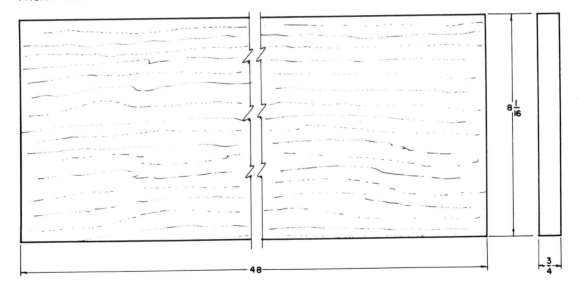

$8\frac{1}{16}$

48

$\frac{3}{4}$

(40) <u>HOOD MATERIAL</u>
I REQ'D

SIDE VIEW

GLUE IN PLACE

⑩

㊴

㊳

FRONT VIEW

⑩

㊶ <u>SUBASSEMBLY</u>
I REQ'D

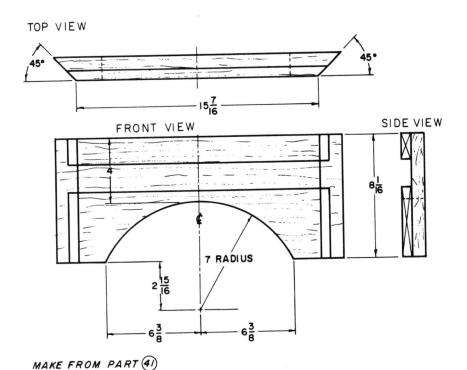

TOP VIEW

$15\frac{7}{16}$

FRONT VIEW

SIDE VIEW

4

$8\frac{1}{16}$

¢

7 RADIUS

$2\frac{15}{16}$

$6\frac{3}{8}$ $6\frac{3}{8}$

MAKE FROM PART ㊷

㊷ HOOD FRONT

I REQ'D

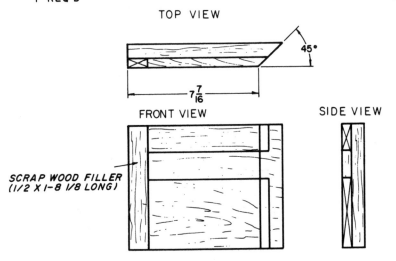

TOP VIEW

45°

$7\frac{7}{16}$

FRONT VIEW

SIDE VIEW

SCRAP WOOD FILLER
(1/2 X 1-8 1/8 LONG)

CUT FROM PART ㊶

㊸ HOOD SIDE

I REQ'D AS SHOWN
I REQ'D OPPOSITE SHOWN

FRONT VIEW

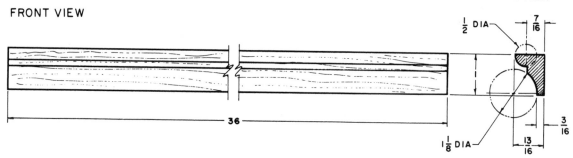

SIDE VIEW

$\frac{1}{2}$ DIA

$\frac{7}{16}$

$1\frac{1}{8}$ DIA

$\frac{3}{16}$

$\frac{13}{16}$

36

(44) HOOD MOLDING
    1 REQ'D

TOP VIEW

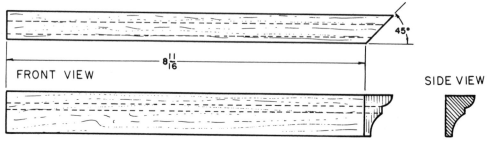

FRONT VIEW

$8\frac{11}{16}$

45°

SIDE VIEW

CUT FROM PART (44)

(45) HOOD MOLDING SIDE
     1 REQ'D AS SHOWN
     1 REQ'D OPPOSITE SHOWN

TOP VIEW

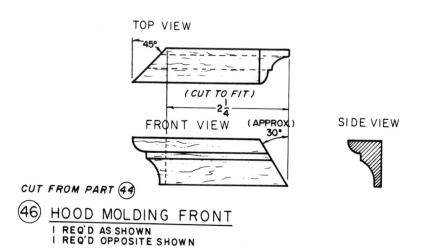

45°

(CUT TO FIT)

$2\frac{1}{4}$

FRONT VIEW

(APPROX.)
30°

SIDE VIEW

CUT FROM PART (44)

(46) HOOD MOLDING FRONT
     1 REQ'D AS SHOWN
     1 REQ'D OPPOSITE SHOWN

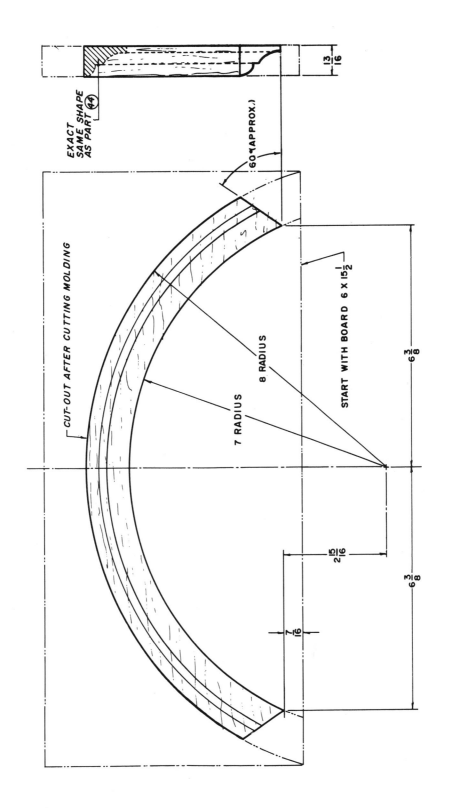

EXACT SAME SHAPE AS PART 44

$\frac{13}{16}$

60° (APPROX.)

CUT-OUT AFTER CUTTING MOLDING

START WITH BOARD 6 X 15$\frac{1}{2}$

8 RADIUS

7 RADIUS

6$\frac{3}{8}$

6$\frac{3}{8}$

2$\frac{15}{16}$

$\frac{7}{16}$

47 CENTER HOOD MOLDING 1 REQ'D

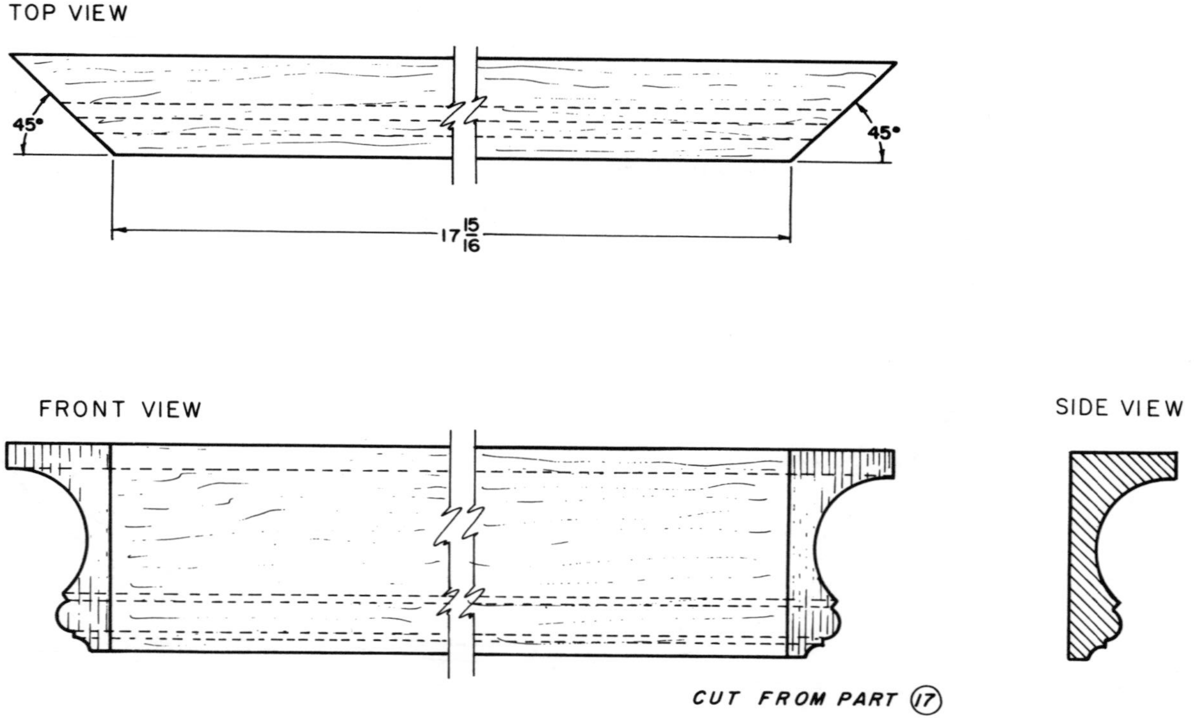

SIDE VIEW

TOP VIEW

45°

45°

17 15/16

FRONT VIEW

CUT FROM PART (17)

(48) HOOD MOLDING

I REQ'D

SIDE VIEW

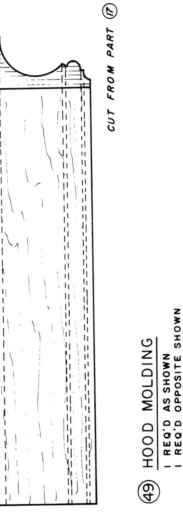

TOP VIEW

45°

$8\frac{11}{16}$

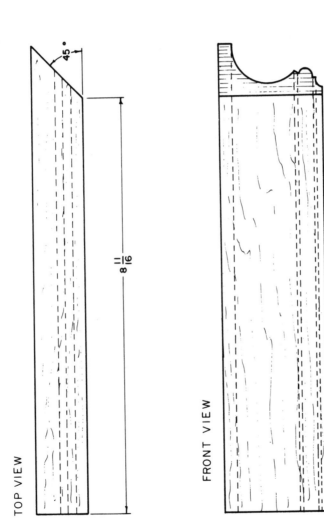

FRONT VIEW

CUT FROM PART ⑰

㊾ HOOD MOLDING

1 REQ'D AS SHOWN
1 REQ'D OPPOSITE SHOWN

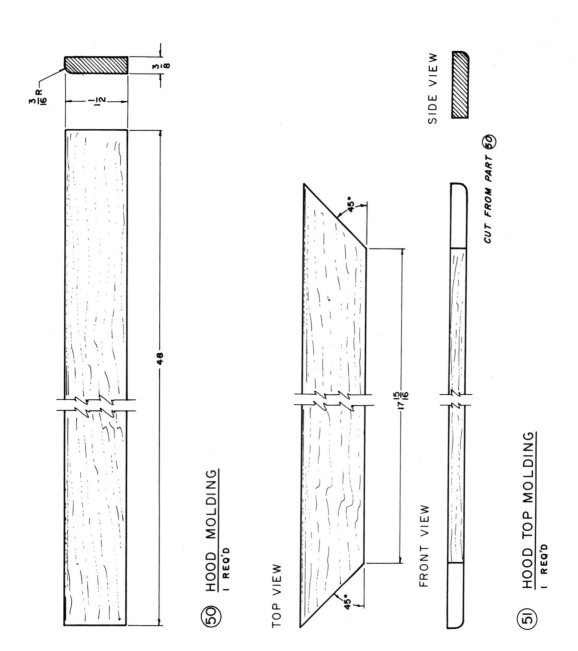

$\frac{3}{16}$ R

$1\frac{1}{2}$

$\frac{3}{8}$

48

(50) HOOD MOLDING
1 REQ'D

TOP VIEW

45°

45°

$17\frac{15}{16}$

FRONT VIEW

SIDE VIEW

CUT FROM PART (50)

(51) HOOD TOP MOLDING
1 REQ'D

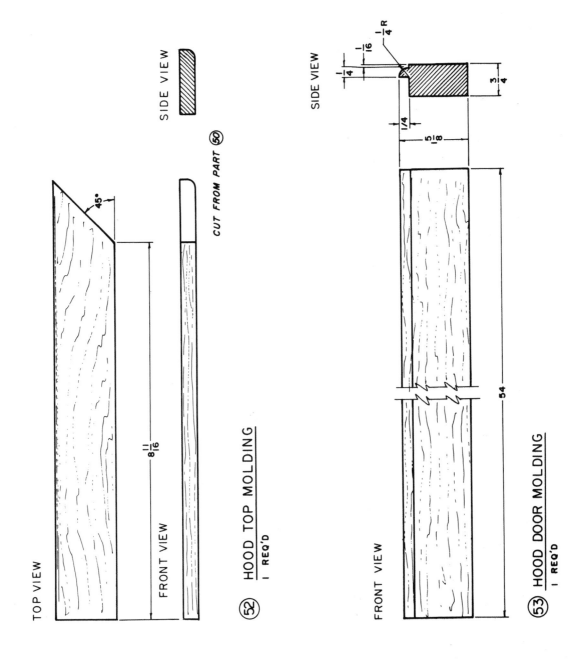

TOP VIEW

SIDE VIEW

45°

$8\frac{11}{16}$

FRONT VIEW

CUT FROM PART ⑤⓪

㉜ HOOD TOP MOLDING
1 REQ'D

SIDE VIEW

$\frac{1}{4}$ R

$\frac{1}{16}$

$\frac{1}{4}$

$\frac{3}{4}$

1/4

$5\frac{1}{8}$

54

FRONT VIEW

㉝ HOOD DOOR MOLDING
1 REQ'D

87

TOP VIEW

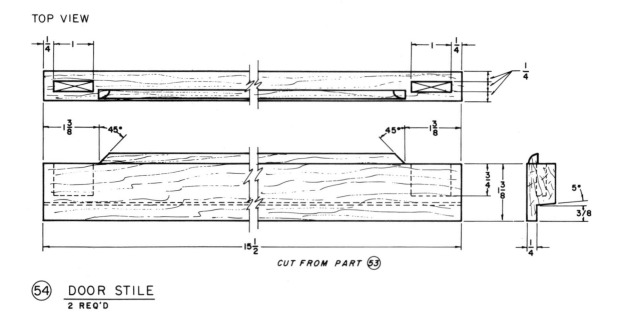

CUT FROM PART ⑤③

⑤④ DOOR STILE
2 REQ'D

FRONT VIEW   SIDE VIEW

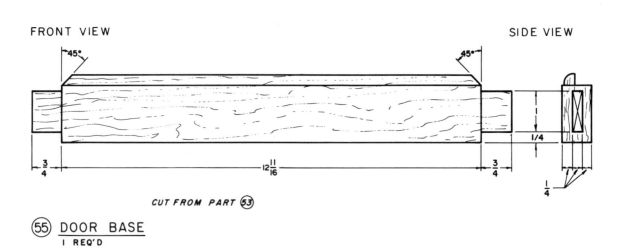

CUT FROM PART ⑤③

⑤⑤ DOOR BASE
1 REQ'D

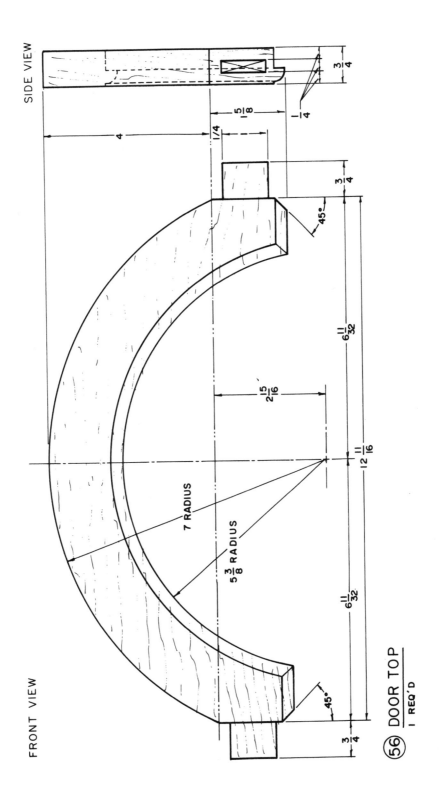

SIDE VIEW

FRONT VIEW

7 RADIUS

$5\frac{3}{8}$ RADIUS

$2\frac{15}{16}$

$6\frac{11}{32}$

$6\frac{11}{32}$

$12\frac{11}{16}$

4

$5\frac{1}{8}$

1/4

$\frac{3}{4}$

$1\frac{1}{4}$

$\frac{3}{4}$

$\frac{3}{4}$

45°

45°

(56) DOOR TOP
1 REQ'D

FRONT VIEW

SIDE VIEW

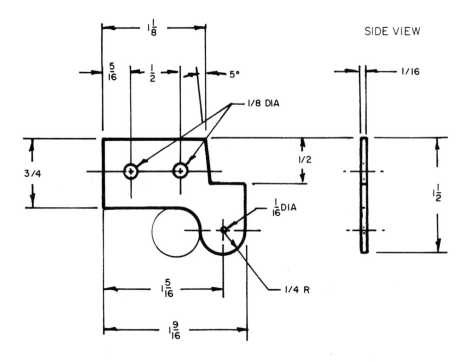

$1\frac{1}{8}$

$\frac{5}{16}$ $\frac{1}{2}$ 5°

1/8 DIA

1/16

1/2

3/4

$1\frac{1}{2}$

$\frac{1}{16}$ DIA

$1\frac{5}{16}$

1/4 R

$1\frac{9}{16}$

(57) HINGE
I REQ'D

TOP VIEW

BRASS SCREW-3/4 LONG-4 REQ'D

$15\frac{7}{16}$

FRONT VIEW

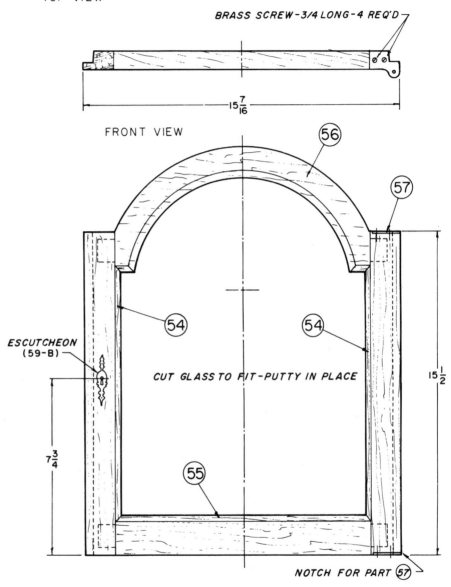

(56)

(57)

(54)   (54)

ESCUTCHEON
(59-B)

CUT GLASS TO FIT-PUTTY IN PLACE

$15\frac{1}{2}$

$7\frac{3}{4}$

(55)

NOTCH FOR PART (57)

(58A) <u>SUB-ASSEMBLY</u>
       I REQ'D

'ROUND' INSIDE TOP EDGE AS REQUIRED
TO FIT INTO HOOD

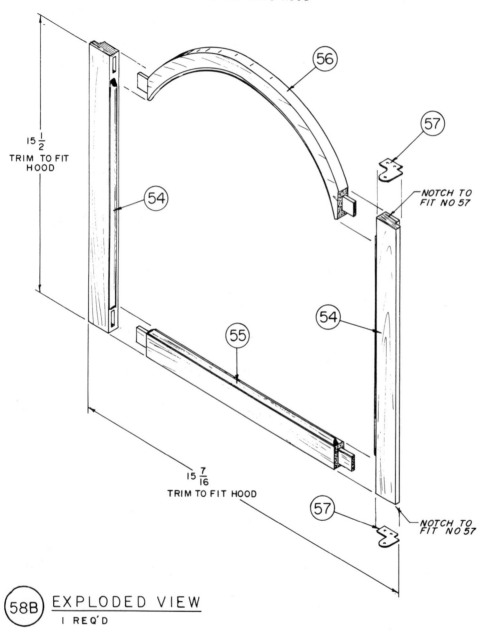

56

57

15 $\frac{1}{2}$
TRIM TO FIT
HOOD

54

NOTCH TO
FIT NO 57

54

55

15 $\frac{7}{16}$
TRIM TO FIT HOOD

57

NOTCH TO
FIT NO 57

58B EXPLODED VIEW
I REQ'D

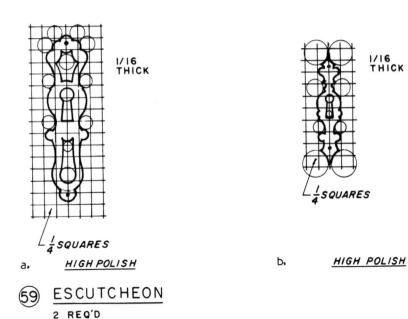

1/16 THICK

1/4 SQUARES

a. HIGH POLISH

1/4 SQUARES

b. HIGH POLISH

(59) ESCUTCHEON
2 REQ'D

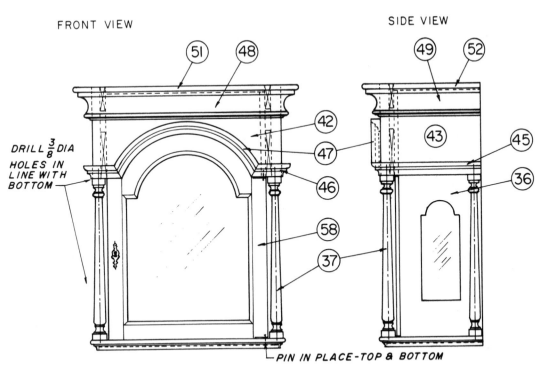

FRONT VIEW

SIDE VIEW

51　48

49　52

42
47
46
58
37

43
45
36

DRILL 3/8 DIA
HOLES IN
LINE WITH
BOTTOM

PIN IN PLACE-TOP & BOTTOM

(60) HOOD ASSEMBLY
1 REQ'D

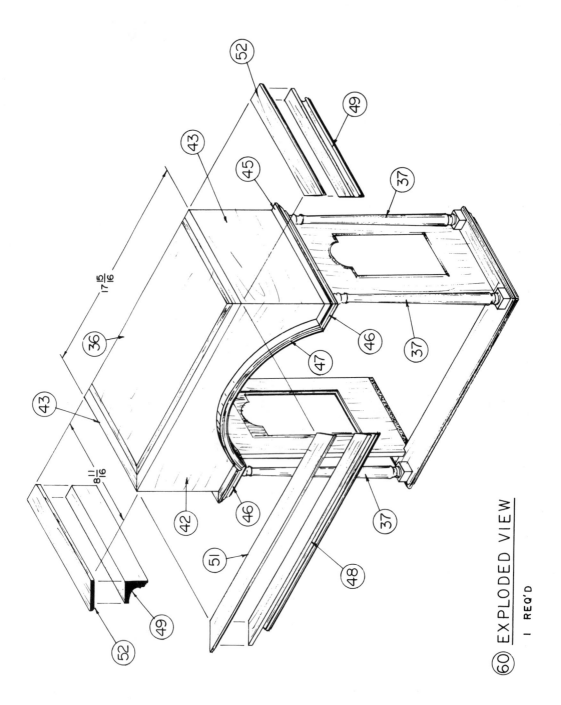

60 EXPLODED VIEW

I REQ'D

94

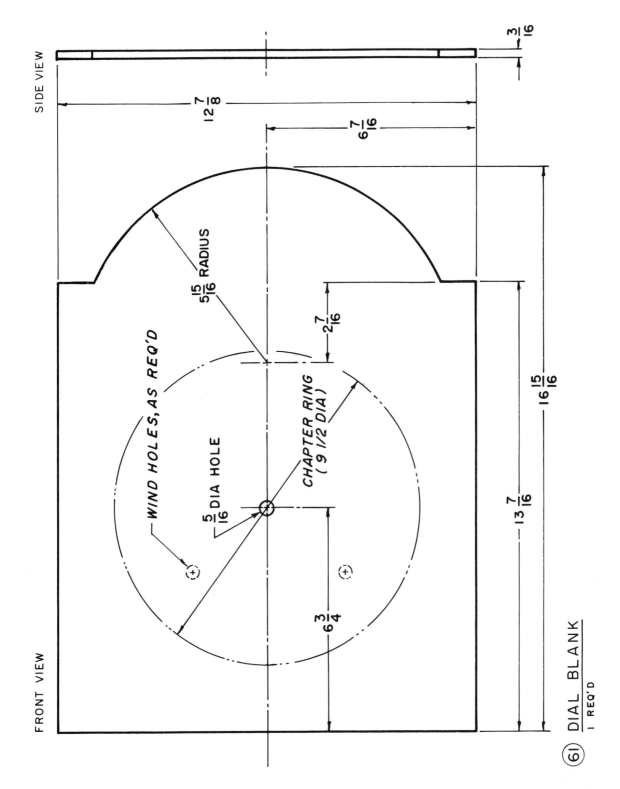

SIDE VIEW

FRONT VIEW

$\frac{3}{16}$

$12\frac{7}{8}$

$6\frac{7}{16}$

$5\frac{15}{16}$ RADIUS

WIND HOLES, AS REQ'D

$2\frac{7}{16}$

$16\frac{15}{16}$

CHAPTER RING
(9 1/2 DIA)

$\frac{5}{16}$ DIA HOLE

$13\frac{7}{16}$

$6\frac{3}{4}$

61 DIAL BLANK
I REQ'D

95

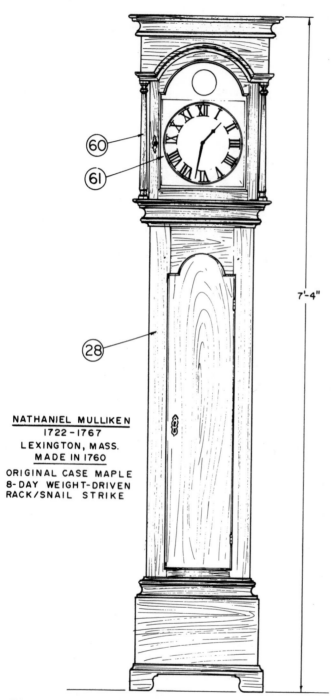

60

61

28

NATHANIEL MULLIKEN
1722 – 1767
LEXINGTON, MASS.
MADE IN 1760

ORIGINAL CASE MAPLE
8-DAY WEIGHT-DRIVEN
RACK/SNAIL STRIKE

7'-4"

62 CLOCK ASSEMBLY

Section IV

FINISHING INSTRUCTIONS

Finishing
Instructions

AFTER COMPLETING YOUR CLOCK, YOU ARE NOW READY TO FINISH IT. THIS is the important part and should not be rushed. Remember, this is the part that will be seen for years to come. No matter how good the wood and hardware you use, or how good the joints are, a poor finish will ruin your project.

Preparing

When finishing your clock, it is very important not to rush. Before applying any stain, you must first prepare the wood. The following preliminaries are imperative to a quality finish.

STEP 1.

All joints should be checked for tight fits. If necessary, apply water putty to all joints, allowing ample time for drying. For this clock, it will not be necessary to set and fill nail heads as they were left showing on the original clock. If, however, you do not want to see the nail heads, set and water putty nail heads, also.

STEP 2.

Sand the clock all over in the direction of the wood grain. If sanding is done by hand, use a sanding block and keep all corners sharp at this time. Sand all over using an 80-grit paper. Resand all over using a 120-grit paper and, if necessary, resand again using a 180-grit paper. Take care not to round edges at this time.

STEP 3.

If you want any of the edges rounded, use the 120-grit paper and later the 180-grit paper, to round the edges.

STEP 4.

This is a 200-year-old clock—antiques should *look* old. A copy of an antique that looks new seems somehow to be a direct contradiction. Distressing can be done many ways. Using a piece of coral stone about 3 inches in diameter, or a similar object, roll the stone across the various surfaces. Don't be afraid to add a few random scratches here and there, especially on the bottoms or backs where an object would have been worn the most. Carefully study the clock and try to imagine how it would have been used through the years. Using a rasp, judiciously round the edges where you think wear would have occurred. Resand the entire project and the new worn edges with 180-grit paper.

STEP 5.

Carefully check that all surfaces are smooth, dry, and dust free, especially if soft wood is used.

Staining

There are two major kinds of stain—water stain and oil stain. Water stains are purchased in powder form and mixed as needed by dissolving the powder in hot water. Water stain has a tendency to raise the grain of the wood. If a water stain is used, when it dries it should be lightly sanded with fine paper. Oil stains are stains from pigments ground in linseed oil and do not raise the grain.

Fillers

A paste filler should be used for porous wood such as oak or mahogany. Purchase paste filler slightly darker than the color of your wood because the new wood you used will turn darker with age. Before using paste filler, thin with turpentine so it can be brushed. Use a stiff brush and brush with the grain in order to fill the pores. After 15 or 20 minutes, wipe off with a piece of burlap across the grain, taking care to leave filler in the pores. Apply a second coat if necessary. Let it dry for 24 hours.

STEP 1.

Test-stain on a scrap piece of the same kind of lumber to make certain it will be the color you wish.

STEP 2.

Wipe or brush on the stain as quickly and as evenly as possible to avoid overlapping streaks. If a darker finish is desired, apply more than one coat of stain. Try not to apply too much stain on the end grain. Allow to dry in a dust-free area for at least 24 hours.

Finishes

Shellac is a hard finish that is easy to apply and dries in a few hours. For best results, thin slightly with alcohol and apply an extra coat or two. Several coats of thin shellac are much better than one or two thick coats. Sand lightly with extra-fine paper between coats but be sure to rub the entire surface with a dampened cloth. Strive for a smooth satin finish—not a high, glossy finish coat—for that antique effect.

Varnish is easy to brush on and dries to a smooth, hard finish within 24 hours. It makes an excellent finish that is transparent and will give a deep finish look to your project. Be sure to apply varnish in a completely dust-free area. Apply one or two coats directly from the can with long, even strokes. Rub between each coat. After the last coat, rub with 0000 steel wool. As with shellac, do not leave a glossy finish. An antique would not have a high gloss finish after 150 years.

Oil finishes are especially easy to use for this project. It is easy to apply, long lasting, never needs resanding, and actually improves wood permanently. Apply a heavy wet coat uniformly to all surfaces and let set for 20 or 30 minutes. Wipe completely dry until you have a nice satin finish.

Wash Coat

Notice, your clock probably still looks "new" even with the distressing marks and scratches. To give your project that 200-year-old look, simply wipe on a coat of oil-base black paint directly from the can with a cloth. Take care to get the black paint in all distress marks and scratches. Wipe off all paint immediately before it dries but leave the black paint in all the corners, joints, scratches, and distress marks. Experiment. If you goof or don't like your results, simply wipe it off using a cloth with turpentine on it. This wash coat should make your project look like the original clock.

Section V

FINAL DETAILS

Final Details

ORIGINAL CLOCKS OF 1760 USUALLY HAD ENGRAVED BRASS DIALS. THIS clock is a departure from that because engraved dials cannot be made by the average woodworker. Painted dials came into use around 1800, so we're 40 years off on the dial face. They are, however, rather simple to do and within the ability of most woodworkers.

Laying Out and Painting the Dial Face

After the dial face blank has been primed, painted, and lightly sanded, it is ready for the numbers and painted flowers. Refer to Illus. F. The numbers are put in using a draftsman's ink pen and an inking compass. The flowers and leaves are put on using simple tole painting or stenciling techniques.

Commercial paper dials can be purchased from one of the many clock suppliers listed at the end of the book, but you will have more satisfaction if you do the entire clock yourself—*including* the dial face. The face is not difficult and, with a little practice, can be done by most anyone. If you study some original clock dial faces you can see they were all done by

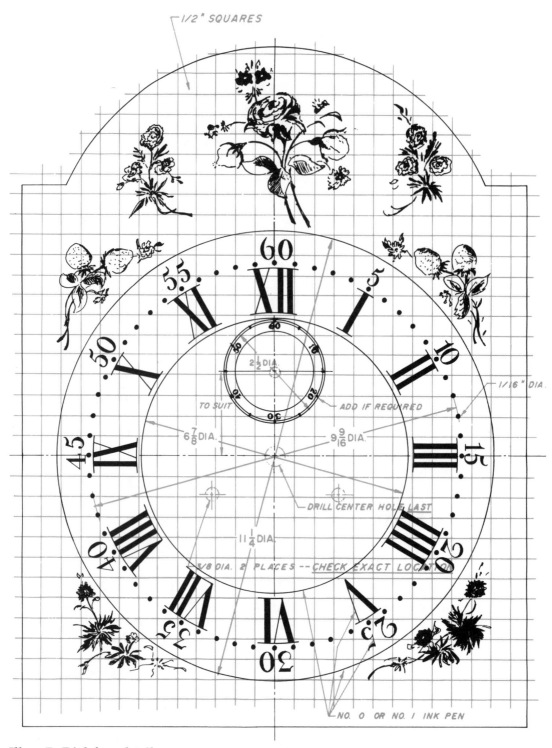

Illus. F. Dial face detail.

hand and are not completely perfect. Try it. If it does not work out, you can always purchase a commercial face. Commercial faces all look new and do not, as a rule, have any "character." When ordering a paper dial, order one with a 9½-inch dial ring.

Note: all lines indicated in the instructions below as "light construction lines" are drawn with an H-grade pencil lead and all inking is done with a no. 0 or no. 1 draftsman's inking pen.

STEP 1.

Lightly draw a 9⁹⁄₁₆-inch-diameter circle from the center of the dial, referring back to the drawing of the dial face blank (no. 61).

STEP 2.

Lightly divide this circle into 12 equal spaces of 30 degrees each.

STEP 3.

Lightly divide the 12 parts into 5 equal spaces of 6 degrees each.

STEP 4.

Using an inking pen, put a ¹⁄₁₆-inch dot at each of these places as shown. This is the hour ring. There should be 60 dots.

STEP 5.

Lightly draw a 9⁵⁄₁₆-inch diameter as a guideline for the top of the hour numbers.

STEP 6.

Lightly draw a 7⅛-inch diameter as a guide for the bottom of the hour numbers.

STEP 7.

Ink in a 6⅞-inch diameter and a 11¼-inch diameter ring as shown.

STEP 8.

Lightly draw a 10¾-inch diameter as a guideline for the top of the minute numbers.

STEP 9.

Lightly draw a 9¾-inch diameter as a guideline for the bottom of the minute numbers.

STEP 10.

Lightly lay out the hour numbers as shown. Note the number 4.

STEP 11.

Lightly lay out the minute numbers as shown.

STEP 12.

Darken in all numbers with an inking pen using a straight-edged plastic triangle for all hour numbers as shown. The minute numbers are inked in by hand.

STEP 13.

Redraw the flowers and leaves on a thin sheet of paper using a ½-inch grid. Locate and transfer the patterns to the dial face using simple tole painting strokes. Paint them to suit yourself, using whatever colors you wish. If you wish to stencil the flowers and leaves, a stencil will have to be cut. Refer to a good stencil book for instructions. These were originally very bright, so don't be afraid to use bright colors.

STEP 14.

Allow the paint to dry for 48 hours and paint the dial face with a light coat of satin finish water varnish, taking care not to smudge the inking. The dial is now ready for the clock.

Installing The Movement And Dial

The movement is a precision instrument that is very delicate, so take extreme care in handling it. A baseboard must be made to fit the movement you are going to use (Illus. G). For movements, I recommend #P-54 from Merritt's Antique, Inc. It has nice movement and is very close

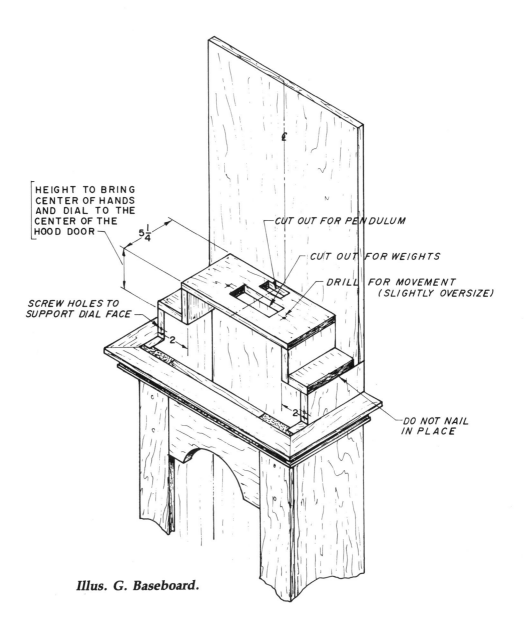

HEIGHT TO BRING
CENTER OF HANDS
AND DIAL TO THE
CENTER OF THE
HOOD DOOR

$5\frac{1}{4}$

CUT OUT FOR PENDULUM

CUT OUT FOR WEIGHTS

DRILL FOR MOVEMENT
(SLIGHTLY OVERSIZE)

SCREW HOLES TO
SUPPORT DIAL FACE

2

2

DO NOT NAIL
IN PLACE

Illus. G. Baseboard.

to original. I also recommend #084069 from S. La Rose, Inc. It is inexpensive and has excellent movement but is not as close to the original.

Instructions to set up and run these movements are not included because they are usually installed by professional clock repairers; however, they are easy to install. Each movement comes with the weights, pendulum, cable pulleys, bell, bell stand, hands, and wind key.

The most common problem with a clock movement is getting the clock

Recommended movement from Merritt's Antiques (# P-54) is an exact copy of those used around 1760.

Courtesy of Merritt's Antiques.

into ''beat''—in other words, getting it to tictoc evenly. This is an easy adjustment to make. After the movement has been installed into your clock case and you have leveled the clock perfectly with a level, hang the pendulum and weights and wind the clock up. Gently start the pendulum swinging and listen to the tictoc. It must be regular. If it is

Movement in place. Note the support for the movement to bring it in line with the dial face.

Note the rough cast-iron weights and the special brass door hinges.

not regular: tic—toc-tic—toc-tic—toc or tic-toc—tic—tic-toc, for instance, it is *out of beat* and must be adjusted. (Some clock movements have a built-in, self-regulating system that do not need adjusting.)

To adjust the clock, carefully bend the crutch to one side until you feel it give slightly. Start the clock and again listen to the beat. If it has been improved, continue until the clock beats perfectly. If you made it worse, bend the crutch in the opposite direction. Once the beat is correct, add the hour hand. This is usually a tight slip-fit. Add the minute hand, which usually fits into a square or rectangular shaft. If your movement has a bell strike, move the minute hand until it strikes and count the strikes. Set the hour hand to this time and adjust the minute hand to 12 o'clock. Slowly turn the minute hand around to the next hour to check for correct striking on the hour.

Once the clock is in ''beat'' and the hands are on, set the correct time and let it run for 24 hours. If it is running too *fast,* lower the pendulum bob by turning the round nut below the pendulum bob a turn or two. If it is running too *slow,* raise the pendulum bob. Remember: *up* for speed up; *down* for slow down. Let the clock run for 24 more hours and note if it has gained or lost time. Readjust until the clock keeps perfect time.

Make a paper pattern of the center hole and the two winding holes and double-check for accuracy. If correct, transfer the location of the two winding holes to the dial face and drill the two winding holes. Remove the hands and attach the dial face to the baseboard with two flat-head brass screws, one on each side. Add the hands and recheck that the clock is striking correctly. Adjust if necessary.

The movement comes already oiled but must be reoiled every 5 years or so. Use only *clock oil* and apply very lightly only where the shafts contact the plates. Remember: too much oil is just as bad as no oil at all.

Appendix I

Antique Hardware and Accessories Suppliers

The extra money spent on hardware of high-quality versus low-cost hardware is very little in the overall cost of your clock. This is the part of the clock that is most noticed, so the extra spent in cost will be well worth the difference for many years to come.

Listed below are quality vendors that sell authentic, high-quality hardware. It is best to use the same kind of hardware as was used on the original clock, if possible. Another good place to purchase old hardware is a flea market. An old authentic hinge or door lock, although rusty and worn, will add a lot of authenticity to your project and will really make it look original.

Bevelled Glass

Beveled Glass Works
11721 S.E. Talor
Portland, OR 97216

Measured Drawings (of Antiques)

Caryle Lynch
196 Holly Hill
Broadway, VA 22815

John A. Nelson
220 General Miller Rd.
Peterborough, NH 03458

Paint

Cohassett Colonials
Cohassett, MA 02025

Stulb Paint and Chemical Co. Inc.
P.O. Box 297
Norristown, PA 19404

Stains/Tung Oil

Cohassett Colonials
Cohassett, MA 02025

Deft Inc.
17451 Von Darman Ave.
Irvine, CA 92713-9507

Formby's Inc.
825 Crossover Lane, Suite 240
Memphis, TN 38117

Stulb Paint and Chemical Co. Inc.
P.O. Box 297
Norristown, PA 19404

Watco-Dennis Corp.
Michigan Ave. & 22nd St.
Santa Monica, CA 90404

Old-Fashioned Nails/Brass Screws

Equality Screw Co. Inc.
P.O. Box 1296
El Cajon, CA 92002

Horton Brasses
P.O. Box 95 Nooks Hill Rd.
Cromwell, CT 06416

Tremont Nail Co.
P.O. Box 111, 21 Elm St.
Wareham, MA 02571

Brasses

Anglo-American Brass Co.
P.O. Box 9792, 4146 Mitzi Drive
San Jose, CA 95157-0792

Ball and Ball
463 W. Lincoln Hwy.
Exton, PA 19341

The Brass Tree
308 N. Main St.
Charles, MO 63301

Garrett Wade Co. Inc.
161 Avenue of the Americas
New York, NY 10013

Heirloom Antiques Brass Co.
P.O. Box 146
Dundass, MN 55019

Horton Brasses
P.O. Box 95 Nooks Hill Rd.
Cromwell, CT 06416

Imported European Hardware
4295 S. Arville
Las Vegas, NV 89103

19th Century Co. Hardware Supply Co.
P.O. Box 599
Rough and Ready, CA 95975

The Renovators' Supply
Millers Falls, MA 01349

The Shop, Inc.
P.O. Box 3711, R.D. 3
Reading, PA 19606

Ritter and Son Hardware
Dept. WJ
Gualala, CA 95445

Veneering

Bob Morgan Woodworking Supplies
1123 Bardstown Rd.
Louisville, KY 40204

General Catalogs

Brookstone Co.
Vose Farm Rd.
Peterborough, NH 03458

Constantine
2050 Eastchester Rd.
Bronx, NY 10461

Cryder Creek Wood Shoppe, Inc.
P.O. Box 19
Whitesville, NY 14897

The Fine Tool Shops
P.O. Box 1262, 20 Backus Ave.
Danbury, CT 06810

Leichtung Inc.
4944 Commerce Pkwy.
Cleveland, OH 44128

Silvo Hardware Co.
2205 Richmond St.
Philadelphia, PA 19125

Trendlines
375 Beacham St.
Chelsea, MA 02150

Woodcraft
P.O. Box 4000, 41 Atlantic Ave.
Woburn, MA 01888

The Woodworkers Store
21801 Industrial Blvd.
Rogers, MN 55374

Woodworkers Supply of New Mexico
5604 Alameda N.E.
Albuquerque, NM 87113

Clock Supplies

Empire Clock Inc.
1295 Rice St.
St. Paul, MN 55117

H.De Covnick and Son
P.O. Box 68
Alamo, CA 94507

Klockit
P.O. Box 629
Lake Geneva, WI 53147

Kuempel Chime Clock Works
21195 Monnetonka Blvd.
Excelsior, MN 55331-8605

Mason and Sullivan and Co.
586 Higgins Crowell Rd.
West Yarmouth, MA 02673

Merritt Antiques Inc.
R.D. 2
Douglassville, PA 19518

S. Larose Inc.
234 Commerce Place
Greensborough, NC 27420

Turncraft Clock Imports Co.
6540 Plymouth Ave. North
Golden Valley, MN 55427

Westwood Clock 'N Kits
2850-B East 29th St.
Long Beach, CA 90806

Appendix II

National Clock Association

In the event you really get the "clock-bug" you might wish to join the national Association of Watch and Clock Collectors, Inc. (NAWCC) of 514 Popular Street, Columbia, PA 17512. This is a National organization devoted solely to horology—the art of clock and watch making. It has a national network of local clock clubs throughout the country that hold meetings in order to help each other with clock problems, study the history of clocks, buy and sell clocks of all descriptions to each other, and teach each other various aspects of clock making and repair. It is a great organization to belong to if you are interested in clocks.

Clock Repair

Another aspect of clocks is clock repair. Years ago I took a clock repair home study course from the SCHOOL OF CLOCK REPAIR of 6313 Come About Way, P.O. Box 315, Awendaw SC 29429. It was by far the best course I have ever taken and it really got me going on clock repair. If interested, you might want to write them for details and a brochure on the course outline and costs.

Glossary

arbor—A steel shaft on which the wheels and pinions are affixed.

boss—An attachment to a dial, usually round, on which the clockmaker's name and town is shown.

bushing—An insert of hard material in a clock plate at the point of arbor pivot to allow for additional wear.

chapter—The ring on the dial plate on which are painted or engraved the hour numerals and minute graduations.

collet—A brass collar that holds a wheel on the arbor.

cock—A bracket from which the pendulum hangs.

count wheel—A wheel with spaced slots that indexes the correct number of blows the hammer makes on the bell when the clock is striking.

crutch wire—A wire that carries the impulse from the escapement to the pendulum.

dial arch—The arched portion at the top of many dials. May contain a boss, a moon dial, or decoration. If the dial is square, this is omitted.

dial foot—A pillar on the back of a dial for attaching the dial to a false plate or movement.

dial plate—A plate, usually brass, iron, or wood, on which the dial is engraved or painted.

escapement—A device by which the pendulum controls the rate of timekeeping. It consists of an anchor and an escape wheel.

escape wheel—A wheel at the end of the wheel train that is engaged by the anchor to regulate the clock's running.

false plate—An intermediate plate between the movement and dial on some clocks to aid fitting the dial to the movement.

fly—A wind-resistant fan that regulates the speed of striking.

gear—*See wheel.*

great gear—The first wheel in a train to which is usually attached the arbor, winding drum, and weight.

moon dial—A dial often found in the arch portion of a clock dial that indicates the cycle of the moon.

motion train—A series of wheels that regulate the rotation of the hour and minute hands.

pendulum—A swinging device attached to the escapement by means of the crutch that controls the rate of timekeeping.

pillar—A turned post of metal or wood that connects to the front and back plates and establishes a fixed distance between them.

pinion—A small gear with twelve or less teeth, called leaves, that meshes with larger gears.

pivot—A round hole in a clock plate in which an arbor end rotates.

plates—Two parallel pieces of metal or wood between which the gears, pinions, and arbors are fitted.

rack and snail—An indexing system for striking that sets itself for correct striking shortly before striking begins.

seat board—A wooden board on which a clock movement sits when in a case.

sprandrels—Painted or cast-metal decoration for dials.

trains—A series of gears and pinions through which power is transmitted from the weights to the escapement.

verge—A device that regulates the speed of rotation of the escape wheel.

wheel—A circular piece of metal on the perimeter of which are cut teeth. Also called *gear*.

winding drum (barrel)—A cylinder onto which the cord holding the weight is wound.

Index

V

varnish, 101
veneering, suppliers of, 120
verge, 15

W

waist, 11
  front molding for, 62
  molding for, 61
side molding for, 63
wash coat, 102
water stain, 100
weights, 113
wheels, 13
Willard, Benjamin, 5
Willard, Ephrim, 5
winding arbors, 12
wooden movements
  early clocks, 5
  long-case clocks, 13

Edited by Joanne M. Slike

NOTES

NOTES